THE ULTIMATE
REAL MADRID
TRIVIA BOOK

A Collection of Amazing Trivia Quizzes
and Fun Facts for Die-Hard Los Blancos Fans!

Ray Walker

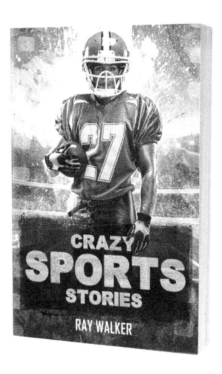

CONTENTS

INTRODUCTION

From their humble beginnings in 1902 to the present day, Real Madrid has blazed a path of glory in the world of sports by becoming one of the most successful and richest soccer clubs on the planet. With a remarkable record of 13 European Cups/Champions League titles under their belt and more than 30 La Liga championships, the Spanish club stands second to none in its homeland.

Typically known as Los Blancos by their passionate and loyal fans, Real Madrid has been setting records consistently for well over a century now, and there's no indication that it's ever going to end.

The club has one of the biggest worldwide followings due to its never-say-die attitude and the endless and entertaining amount of skill it displays on the pitch week after week.

It's no wonder the squad has never ever been relegated, with legendary players and managers such as Cristiano Ronaldo, Santiago Bernabéu, Raymond Kopa, Alfredo Di Stéfano, Francisco Gento, Ferenc Puskás, Ronaldo, Iker Casillas, Sergio Ramos, Zinedine Zidane, David Beckham, Roberto Carlos, Toni Kroos, Clarence Seedorf, Gareth Bale, Eden Hazard,

Hugo Sánchez, Carlo Ancelotti, Arthur Johnson, and Vicente del Bosque.

Los Blancos have had to put in the work for all their success, though, because nothing comes easy when competing in the Spanish La Liga and European Champions League, especially with rivals such as Barcelona, Atlético Madrid, Athletic Bilbao, Bayern Munich, and Juventus, among others.

The team's supporters don't take defeat lightly and expect nothing but an honest effort from every player who wears Real Madrid's famous white kit.

This trivia and fact book was written in celebration and honor of the club's amazing achievements by looking back at its history from the beginning right up until February 2021. You'll read about the side's best players and managers and be reminded of the record-setting events over the past century or so.

Real Madrid's remarkable history is presented here in quiz form with 12 chapters, each featuring a unique topic. Each chapter contains 20 stimulating but lighthearted quiz questions along with 10 educational "Did You Know" facts. There are multiple-choice and true-false questions in each chapter, and the answers are available on a separate page.

For those fans who would like to learn as much as possible about Real Madrid, we feel this is the ideal book to achieve that goal. When you've finished reading, you'll be fully prepared to share and show off your knowledge by challenging fellow fans to trivia showdowns.

CHAPTER 1:

ORIGINS & HISTORY

QUIZ TIME!

1. What year was Real Madrid CF founded?

    a. 1910
    b. 1906
    c. 1902
    d. 1887

2. The crown on the club's crest is the crown of King Alfonso XIII, who gave the club the title "Real" (meaning "Royal") in the 1920s.

    a. True
    b. False

3. What site did the club call home for 11 years starting in 1912?

    a. Estadio Chamartín
    b. Campo de O'Donnell
    c. El Soto
    d. Campo de Madrid

4. Who scored the first goal ever for the team in a competitive match?

    a. Pedro Parages
    b. Arthur Johnson
    c. Manolo Mendía
    d. Adolfo Meléndez

5. What year did the club play its first game at Santiago Bernabéu Stadium?

    a. 1961
    b. 1957
    c. 1955
    d. 1947

6. Which of the following is NOT one of Madrid's nicknames?

    a. Los Merengues
    b. Los Blancos
    c. Los Reales
    d. Los Vikingos

7. Real Madrid participated in five competitions in the club's inaugural year.

    a. True
    b. False

8. Which club did Real play against in its first friendly match?

    a. RCD Espanyol
    b. Club Retiro

    c. Iberia FC

    d. New Foot-Ball Club

9. How many years was club legend Santiago Bernabéu president of Real Madrid?

    a. 62

    b. 50

    c. 40

    d. 35

10. Real Madrid's first competitive match was a loss to which club?

    a. Iberia FC

    b. Club Español de Madrid

    c. FC Barcelona

    d. Moncloa FC

11. The inaugural match held at Santiago Bernabéu Stadium was played against which Portuguese club?

    a. Sporting CP

    b. C.F. Os Belenenses

    c. S.L. Benfica

    d. FC Porto

12. Real Madrid was one of the few teams that did not participate in the inaugural season of La Liga.

    a. True

    b. False

13. Which club did Real defeat for its first official victory in a competitive match?

    a. FC Barcelona
    b. Athletic Bilbao
    c. RCD Espanyol
    d. Moderno FC

14. How many friendly matches did the side play in its first official year?

    a. 4
    b. 7
    c. 10
    d. 14

15. Madrid's first La Liga match was against which club?

    a. Atlético Madrid
    b. Real Unión
    c. CE Europa
    d. Real Sociedad

16. Real Madrid's home kits have always featured a white shirt since the club's inception.

    a. True
    b. False

17. Who scored the club's first goal ever in La Liga?

    a. Jaime Lazcano
    b. Juan Monjardín
    c. Gaspar Rubio
    d. Rafael Morera

18. What was the outcome of Madrid's first La Liga match?

    a. 3-1 win
    b. 2-4 loss
    c. 5-0 win
    d. 2-2 draw

19. Who were two of Real Madrid's key founders?

    a. Julián Palacios and Juan Padrós
    b. Adolfo Meléndez and Luis de Urquijo
    c. Julián Palacios and Pedro Parages
    d. Juan Padrós and Carlos Da Silva

20. Santiago Bernabéu Stadium is the largest football stadium in Spain.

    a. True
    b. False

QUIZ ANSWERS

1. C – 1902

2. A – True

3. B – Campo de O'Donnell

4. B – Arthur Johnson

5. D – 1947

6. C – Los Reales

7. B – False

8. D – New Foot-Ball Club

9. D – 35

10. C – FC Barcelona

11. B – C.F. Os Belenenses

12. B – False

13. C – RCD Espanyol

14. C – 10

15. C – CE Europa

16. A – True

17. A – Jaime Lazcano

18. C – 5-0 win

19. A – Julián Palacios and Juan Padrós

20. B – False

DID YOU KNOW?

1. Real Madrid Club de Fútbol plays in the Primera División of the Spanish La Liga and is known by several nicknames, including Los Blancos (The Whites), Los Merengues (The Meringues), Los Vikingos (The Vikings), and La Casa Blanca (The White House). The organization was founded on March 6, 1902, as the Madrid Football Club. The club is also home to several other sporting entities, including basketball and women's football, and it used to feature departments for handball, rugby union, and volleyball.

2. The origins of Real Madrid stretch back to when soccer was introduced to the city by students of the Institución Libre de Enseñanza, many of whom were graduates of Oxford and Cambridge Universities in England. In 1897, the students founded an organization named Sky Football, which was commonly known as La Sociedad (The Society). This was the only soccer club in Madrid at the time. It played matches on Sunday mornings. The club split up in 1900, and several members formed a new club named Nueva Sociedad de Football (New Society of Football).

3. Members of the Nueva Sociedad de Football included Julián Palacios, Juan Padrós, and Carlos Padrós. Palacios was later considered the first unofficial president of Real Madrid because he was in charge from 1900 to 1902, while the Padrós brothers would become presidents further

down the road. In 1901, the members of Nueva Sociedad de Football renamed it the Madrid Football Club, and a year later, it became an official organization with Juan Padrós being elected the head of the board as president.

4. Madrid FC won its first silverware in 1905 by downing Athletic Bilbao in the Spanish Cup final. In January 1909, the club became one of the founding members of the Royal Spanish Football Federation. Its first official home ground was Campo de O'Donnell, where the side moved in 1912 after previously playing home matches at various venues. The club's name was then changed to Real Madrid in 1920 by King Alfonso XIII.

5. The first major national Spanish football league was founded in 1929 and became known as La Liga. Real Madrid led the league during the inaugural campaign until the final game, when a defeat to Athletic Bilbao gave Barcelona the title with Real finishing runner-up. Real Madrid captured its first league championship in 1931-32 and successfully defended it the following season to become the first La Liga side to claim the title twice. In April 1931, the club temporarily lost the "Real" title due to the arrival of the Second Spanish Republic and was once again known simply as the Madrid Football Club.

6. In 1945, Santiago Bernabéu was named club president and had the team's new stadium built as Estadio Real Madrid Club de Fútbol, later to be renamed after Bernabéu. The Ciudad Deportiva training venue was also erected. Several

years later, the Real Madrid youth academy was founded and was known as "Cantera." It is now called "La Fábrica." Beginning in 1953, the club began signing top-ranked players from elsewhere in the world, such as Alfredo Di Stéfano of Argentina.

7. A tournament for European club champions was organized in 1955 with various league winners being invited. This event would later evolve into the European Cup/UEFA Champions League. Real Madrid became a major force nationally and in Europe as the club won five consecutive European Cups, reaching the final seven times. The team also captured five La Liga titles in a seven-year span with the help of legendary squad players such as Raymond Kopa, Alfredo Di Stéfano, Francisco Gento, and Ferenc Puskás.

8. Real Madrid averages the second-highest attendances in Spanish soccer behind Barcelona. Most home matches are attended by season ticket-holders, the number of which is limited to 65,000. A fan must first be a club member before acquiring a season ticket, and the waiting list is usually long. The team's hardcore fans are typically known as Ultras Sur or Ultras.

9. Real Madrid is listed as a registered association, which means the organization is owned by its members who elect the club president. Shares can't be purchased, only memberships. The club president isn't allowed to invest his or her own money in the club, and the outfit is only

allowed to spend money that it earns. Revenues are generally earned through broadcasting rights, tickets, and merchandise sales.

10. The club's women's soccer team is known as Real Madrid Club de Fútbol Femenino, and its nickname is Las Blancas (The Whites). The club was founded in September 2014 and plays its home matches at Ciudad Real Madrid, which is the men's senior team's training facility. The side competes in the Primera División and was originally founded as an independent entity known as Club Deportivo Tacón. It was acquired by Real Madrid in 2019 and re-branded as Real Madrid's women's football.

CHAPTER 2:

THE CAPTAIN CLASS

QUIZ TIME!

1. Which of these players was NOT named vice-captain in 2015?

   a. Marcelo

   b. Raphaël Varane

   c. Karim Benzema

   d. Isco

2. José Berraondo was the club's first-ever full-time captain.

   a. True

   b. False

3. Which player was never named a full-time captain of Real Madrid?

   a. Cristiano Ronaldo

   b. Fernando Hierro

   c. Amancio Amaro

   d. Pirri

4. Who was named captain in 2010?

    a. Iker Casillas
    b. Pepe
    c. Jerzy Dudek
    d. Ricardo Carvalho

5. How many full-time captains did the side appoint between 2000 and 2010?

    a. 7
    b. 5
    c. 3
    d. 2

6. Who captained the team from 1974 to 1976?

    a. Manuel Velázquez
    b. Amancio Amaro
    c. Günter Netzer
    d. Juan Carlos Touriño

7. Eugenio Hilario was the club's first captain in the La Liga era.

    a. True
    b. False

8. Which captain's son also starred for Real Madrid several years later?

    a. Raúl
    b. Sergio Ramos
    c. Manuel Sanchís
    d. Iker Casillas

9. Which player was NOT one of the vice-captains in 2011-12?

    a. Mesut Özil
    b. Sergio Ramos
    c. Marcelo
    d. Gonzalo Higuaín

10. Which player was appointed captain after Amancio Amaro retired?

    a. Francisco Aguilar
    b. Juan Sol
    c. Francisco Uría
    d. Pirri

11. Whom did Manuel Sanchís succeed as captain?

    a. Hugo Sánchez
    b. Chendo
    c. José Antonio Camacho
    d. Míchel

12. Real Madrid has had a total of 43 full-time captains as of 2021.

    a. True
    b. False

13. Which player succeeded Pirri as captain?

    a. Isidro
    b. Pérez García
    c. Santillana
    d. Miguel Ángel

14. What year was Raúl appointed full-time skipper?

    a. 2003

    b. 2005

    c. 2007

    d. 2009

15. Who was handed the armband after Iker Casillas departed?

    a. Gonzalo Higuaín

    b. Marcelo

    c. Karim Benzema

    d. Sergio Ramos

16. Former captain Fernando Hierro left the club in 2003 to play in Qatar.

    a. True

    b. False

17. Who was recognized as the club's first full-time captain?

    a. José Giralt

    b. Arthur Johnson

    c. Federico Revuelto

    d. Santiago Bernabéu

18. What year was Sergio Ramos appointed captain of the club?

    a. 2020

    b. 2017

    c. 2015

    d. 2012

19. How many seasons did Raúl captain Madrid?

    a. 3

    b. 7

    c. 1

    d. 8

20. José Santamaría was the first captain of Real Madrid who was not born in Spain.

    a. True

    b. False

QUIZ ANSWERS

1. D – Isco

2. B – False

3. A – Cristiano Ronaldo

4. A – Iker Casillas

5. D – 2

6. B – Amancio Amaro

7. B – False

8. C – Manuel Sanchís

9. A – Mesut Özil

10. D – Pirri

11. B – Chendo

12. B – False

13. D – Miguel Ángel

14. A – 2003

15. D – Sergio Ramos

16. A – True

17. B – Arthur Johnson

18. C – 2015

19. B – 7

20. B – False

DID YOU KNOW?

1. There have been approximately 30 full-time captains in the history of Real Madrid through February 2021, and several players have also served as vice-captains since the 1990s. Arthur Johnson of Ireland, who was also the club's first manager from 1910 to 1920, is listed as the first captain. He held the position when the club was formed in 1902.

2. The following is a list of the team's full-time captains and the years it's believed they wore the armband: Arthur Johnson, 1902; José Giralt, 1902-03; Federico Revuelto, 1903-04; Luciano Lizárraga, 1904-05, José Berraondo, 1905-09; José María Castell, 1914-15; Santiago Bernabéu, 1915-21; Juan Monjardín, 1921-24; Perico Escobal, 1924-27; Félix Pérez, 1927-28; Félix Quesada, 1928-35; Eugenio Hilario, 1935-36; Leoncito, 1939-42; José Ramón Sauto, 1942-44; Juan Antonio Ipiña, 1944-49; Sabino Barinaga, 1949-50; Clemente Fernández, 1950-52; Luis Molowny, 1952-56; Miguel Muñoz, 1956-58; Juanito Alonso, 1958-60; José María Zárraga, 1960-62; Francisco Gento, 1962-71; Ignacio Zoco, 1971-74; Amancio, 1974-76; Jose Pirri, 1976-80; Miguel Ángel, 1980-86; Santillana, 1986-88; José Antonio Camacho, 1988-89; Chendo, 1989-93; Manuel Sanchís, 1993-2001; Fernando Hierro, 2001-03; Raúl, 2003-10; Iker Casillas, 2010-15; and Sergio Ramos, 2015-current.

3. Of all the club's full-time captains, just three have hailed from outside of Spain. These were Arthur Johnson of Dublin, Ireland; Federico Revuelto of Guatemala City, Guatemala, and José Ramón Sauto of Mexico City, Mexico. Revuelto, who was on the club's board of directors, went on to serve as the interim president of Real Madrid in 1916 when Adolfo Meléndez resigned.

4. The first long-term skipper of Los Blancos was José Ángel Berraondo Insausti, who held the job from 1905 to 1909. He managed the side from 1927 to 1929. Insausti led his side to four straight Copa del Rey trophies as a player from 1905 to 1908. After leaving Real Madrid in 1909, the defender played with Real Sociedad until 1913. He also managed that club from 1918 to 1923 and the Spanish national side from 1921 to 1928.

5. Attacker Santiago Bernabéu is one of the most important men in the history of Real Madrid, and the team's current home stadium is now named in his honor. He played with the side from 1911 to 1926, was captain from 1915 to 1921, and managed it between 1926 and 1927. In addition, he was the club president for approximately 35 years, from September 1943 until his death on June 2, 1978. Bernabéu joined the team's youth system in 1909, when he was 14 years old, and he scored 70 goals in 80 games with the senior side after making his debut in 1913-14. He also helped the squad win a Copa del Rey and nine regional championships.

6. Sabino Barinaga was the skipper between 1949 and 1950, which was his last season with the club after joining in 1940. The forward scored 93 goals in 182 games and helped his teammates win three trophies. Barinaga also had the honor of scoring the first goal at the Santiago Bernabéu Stadium when he struck against Belenenses. The versatile player was comfortable in any position on the pitch and started his career in England with Southampton FC when the Spanish Civil War broke out. Barinaga reportedly notched 62 goals in 13 games with the Southampton reserves before returning to Spain.

7. Juan Antonio Ipiña was a Spanish international who played over 300 matches with the club between 1939 and 1949. The powerful midfielder was known for his ball control and strength and is considered by many to be the first great official captain of Real Madrid, wearing the armband from 1944 to 1949. Ipiña joined the side from Atlético Madrid after the Spanish Civil War and won two Copa del Rey titles with the side in 1946 and 1947. He helped manage the club in 1952-53.

8. One of the team's most dependable midfielders from 1962 to 1974 was Spanish international Ignacio Zoco, who was the acting captain between 1971 and 1974 and played 438 games with the side. He won seven La Liga titles, two Copa del Rey trophies, and a European Cup in 1965-66 with Real Madrid before retiring. Zoco was known for his attacking instincts and aerial play and earned the fans'

respect due to his honesty and loyalty. He went out with a bang as Real won the 1974 Copa del Rey 4-0 over Barcelona in his final game.

9. Legendary midfielder José María Zárraga was a Spanish international who played just over 300 contests with Real Madrid between 1951 and 1962 and was listed as being the side's skipper between 1960 and 1962. He was a member of the famous team that won five straight European Cups from 1956 to 1960, and he also helped the squad win 12 other pieces of silverware, including six La Liga titles. Zárraga left the club in 1962 and continued to work as a director and manager with various Spanish clubs.

10. Known simply as "Chendo," Miguel Porlán Noguera was a Spanish international right-back who spent his entire pro career from 1982 to 1998 with Real Madrid and wore the armband between 1989 and 1993. He joined the youth system in 1977 and played with the reserve Castilla team before making his senior debut. Chendo appeared in 497 official matches and 140 friendlies with the team. He helped his side win seven La Liga titles and a European Cup, as well as nine other trophies. After retiring, Chendo became the match day delegate for Real Madrid.

CHAPTER 3:

AMAZING MANAGERS

QUIZ TIME!

1. Who managed the club from 1910 to 1920?

    a. Juan de Cárcer
    b. Arthur Johnson
    c. Santiago Bernabéu
    d. Pedro Llorente

2. Luis Molowny has won the most trophies as Real's manager as of 2020.

    a. True
    b. False

3. Who was the longest-serving manager of Real Madrid as of 2020?

    a. Miljan Miljanić
    b. Vujadin Boškov
    c. Miguel Muñoz
    d. José Mourinho

4. Who was appointed manager following Zinedine Zidane's resignation in 2018?

   a. Julen Lopetegui
   b. Santiago Solari
   c. Robert Firth
   d. Francisco Bru

5. How many trophies did Luis Molowny win as manager of the team?

   a. 8
   b. 3
   c. 6
   d. 11

6. Who replaced Guus Hiddink as manager following Hiddink's midseason termination in 1999?

   a. José Antonio Camacho
   b. Arsenio Iglesias
   c. John Toshack
   d. Jupp Heynckes

7. Between 2000 and 2010, Los Blancos had 13 different managers.

   a. True
   b. False

8. Who succeeded Miguel Muñoz as manager in 1974?

   a. Manuel Fleitas
   b. Luis Carniglia

c. Miljan Miljanić

d. Luis Molowny

9. Who was appointed manager after Luis Molowny in 1986?

    a. Amancio Amaro
    b. Leo Beenhakker
    c. Benito Floro
    d. Radomir Antić

10. Who succeeded Vicente del Bosque as manager in 1994?

    a. Benito Floro
    b. Alfredo Di Stéfano
    c. Leo Beenhakker
    d. Jorge Valdano

11. Who was named manager following Manuel Pellegrini's departure in 2010?

    a. Carlo Ancelotti
    b. José Mourinho
    c. Fábio Capello
    d. Juande Ramos

12. John Toshack had two stints as Madrid's manager.

    a. True
    b. False

13. Who was appointed manager in June 2015?

    a. Rafael Benítez
    b. Zinedine Zidane
    c. Santiago Solari
    d. Juan Armet

14. How many trophies did José Mourinho win with Madrid?

    a. 2
    b. 5
    c. 3
    d. 0

15. Who became manager following Fábio Capello's departure in 2007?

    a. Carlos Queiroz
    b. Manuel Pellegrini
    c. Carlo Ancelloti
    d. Bernd Schuster

16. Zinedine Zidane won the Best FIFA Football Coach award in 2017.

    a. True
    b. False

17. How many trophies did Miguel Muñoz win as Madrid's manager?

    a. 8
    b. 11
    c. 14
    d. 17

18. Which manager won seven trophies with Madrid?

    a. Leo Beenhakker
    b. Miljan Miljanić
    c. Vicente del Bosque
    d. Carlo Ancelotti

19. How many trophies did Manuel Pellegrini win as the side's manager?

    a. 0

    b. 2

    c. 4

    d. 7

20. Juande Ramos had two stints as Real Madrid's manager.

    a. True

    b. False

QUIZ ANSWERS

1. B – Arthur Johnson
2. B – False
3. C – Miguel Muñoz
4. A – Julen Lopetegui
5. A – 8
6. C – John Toshack
7. B – False
8. D – Luis Molowny
9. B – Leo Beenhakker
10. D – Jorge Valdano
11. B – José Mourinho
12. A – True
13. A – Rafael Benítez
14. C – 3
15. D – Bernd Schuster
16. A – True
17. C – 14
18. C – Vicente del Bosque
19. A – 0
20. B – False

DID YOU KNOW?

1. Real Madrid has had approximately 40 full-time and caretaker managers combined from 1910 through February 2021, with some having more than one stint with the club. The first full-time manager is believed to be Arthur Johnson, and the current boss is Zinedine Zidane, who was appointed on March 11, 2019. Zidane was also in charge of the team from January 4, 2016, to May 31, 2018.

2. Arthur Johnson of Ireland was a former goalkeeper who played as a center-forward for Real Madrid. He's credited with scoring the first competitive goal for the club in 1902 in a loss to Barcelona in the Copa de la Coronación. Johnson managed the team from 1910 to 1920 and won a Copa del Rey in 1917, as well as four regional championships after winning four Copas del Rey as a player. He's the second-longest-serving manager of the club and is credited with persuading the side to wear an all-white strip in honor of his favorite British team, Corinthian Casuals.

3. When it comes to winning silverware, the most successful manager has been Miguel Muñoz of Spain. The former Real Madrid midfielder won nine La Liga titles, two Copa del Rey trophies, two European Cups, and an Intercontinental Cup between 1959 and 1974. He took over the team between February 21, 1959, and April 13, 1959, and again from April 13, 1960, to January 15, 1974. This makes Muñoz

the club's longest-serving manager by time and games coached, and he was the first person to win a European Cup as a player and manager.

4. Success followed Vicente del Bosque wherever he went. The native of Spain enjoyed three stints as manager with Real Madrid between 1994 and 1999 and became the most successful manager ever for the Spanish men's national team. He got off to a great start by leading Real to European Champions League titles in 1999-2000 and 2001-02. He also won a pair of La Liga titles with the team, along with four other pieces of silverware and several individual honors. Del Bosque's calm demeanor helped him handle his players' egos, and his squads seemed always to gel perfectly under his watch.

5. Back in 1931-32, when the club was known as Madrid CF, it was managed by former player Lippo Hertzka of Hungary. He helped guide the team through the league campaign without suffering a single defeat as it won its first La Liga title. There were 10 clubs in the league that season, and Los Blancos posted a record of 10 wins and eight draws for 28 points. They edged defending champions Athletic Bilbao by three points to take the crown while scoring 37 goals and conceding a league-low 15, with Manuel Olivares leading the way with 11 goals. Hertzka, who spent 1930 to 1932 with Real Madrid, managed 11 different clubs during his career.

6. Several managers have won individual awards while in charge of Real Madrid. The FIFA World Coach of the

Year/Best FIFA Football Coach winners were José Mourinho for 2010 and Zinedine Zidane for 2017. The UEFA Club Coach of the Year was won by Vicente del Bosque in 2001-02, while the Alf Ramsey Award winners have been del Bosque in 2001-02 and Mourinho for 2010. The IFFHS World's Best Club Coach winners have been del Bosque for 2002, Mourinho for 2012, Carlo Ancelotti for 2014, and Zidane for 2017 and 2018.

7. Although he managed just 75 games with Real Madrid, Manuel Pellegrini of Chile currently holds the best all-time winning percentage at 75%. He was in charge from June 2, 2009, to May 26, 2010, and he posted a record of 36 wins, five draws, and seven losses in 48 games. His squad earned a then club-record 96 points in the 2009-10 La Liga but still finished as runner-up to Barcelona to leave Pellegrini without a trophy in his one season in charge.

8. Right behind Manuel Pellegrini in the club's winning percentage category is Carlo Ancelotti of Italy. He was in charge from June 25, 2013, to May 25, 2015, and posted 89 wins, 14 draws, and 16 defeats in 119 outings, for a 74.79 winning percentage. Ancelotti also guided the side to a Copa del Rey, European Champions League, UEFA Super Cup, and FIFA Club World Cup title. He's currently one of just three managers to win the European Cup/Champions League three times. Bob Paisley also achieved the feat with Liverpool, while Zinedine Zidane has won it three times with Real Madrid and is the only manager to win it three times in a row, which he did from 2016 to 2018.

9. The first of just two English-born managers for Real Madrid was former player Robert Firth, who held the title from 1932 to 1934. He managed 45 games and registered 30 wins, five draws, and 10 losses for a winning percentage of 66.67. Firth led the side to the La Liga title in 1932-33 while finishing as runner-up the next season. He also led the team to two straight Campeonato Regional Centro titles, in 1933 and 1934, and to the 1933 final of the Copa del Presidente de la República, which they lost 2-1 to Athletic Bilbao.

10. Luis Molowny of Spain won his fair share of trophies with Real Madrid in four separate managerial stints between 1974 and 1986 after playing midfield with the side from 1946 to 1957. He won eight pieces of silverware as a player with Real and another eight as manager. While in charge, he guided the team to three La Liga titles, two Copa del Rey and UEFA Cup victories, and a Copa de La Liga championship. Molowny played for the Spanish national squad seven times and also briefly managed the team.

CHAPTER 4:

GOALTENDING GREATS

QUIZ TIME!

1. Which keeper has made the most appearances in all competitions for Real Madrid as of 2021?
   a. Ricardo Zamora
   b. Miguel Ángel
   c. Francisco Buyo
   d. Iker Casillas

2. Thibaut Courtois won the IFFHS World's Best Goalkeeper award in 2019.
   a. True
   b. False

3. How many clean sheets did Diego López record in 36 La Liga matches in 2013-14?
   a. 16
   b. 13
   c. 9
   d. 4

4. Who was the first player for Real Madrid to officially win the Ricardo Zamora Trophy?

    a. Miguel Ángel
    b. José Vicente Train
    c. Antonio Betancort
    d. José Araquistáin

5. Which keeper played all 44 matches in the 1986-87 La Liga season?

    a. Agustín
    b. Miguel Ángel
    c. José Manuel
    d. Paco Buyo

6. Which keeper played 40 matches in the 1996-97 La Liga campaign?

    a. Albano Bizzarri
    b. Pedro Contreras
    c. Bodo Illgner
    d. Santiago Cañizares

7. Iker Casillas made his debut with Real Madrid's first team at the age of 17.

    a. True
    b. False

8. Which keeper recorded seven clean sheets in all competitions in 2017-18?

    a. Luca Zidane
    b. Kiko Casilla

c. Keylor Navas

d. Fernando Pacheco

9. How many times did Iker Casillas win the IFFHS World's Best Goalkeeper award with Madrid?

    a. 5

    b. 7

    c. 4

    d. 8

10. Where did Ricardo Zamora rank in voting for the IFFHS Goalkeeper of the Century award?

    a. 2nd

    b. 3rd

    c. 5th

    d. 7th

11. Which keeper played 45 matches in all competitions in 1984-85?

    a. Mariano García

    b. José Manuel

    c. Agustín

    d. Miguel Ángel

12. In 2019-20, Thibaut Courtois won the Ricardo Zamora Trophy, allowing 20 goals in 34 La Liga games.

    a. True

    b. False

13. Who posted 10 clean sheets in 26 La Liga games in 1997-98?

    a. Pedro Contreras

    b. Santiago Cañizares

    c. Pedro Jaro

    d. Julen Lopetegui

14. How many matches did Iker Casillas play in all competitions for Madrid?

    a. 814

    b. 788

    c. 725

    d. 676

15. Who backed up Iker Casillas for 16 matches in the 2012-13 La Liga season?

    a. Diego López

    b. Keylor Navas

    c. Antonio Adán

    d. Jerzy Dudek

16. Agustín Rodríguez won the Ricardo Zamora Trophy three times.

    a. True

    b. False

17. How many clean sheets did Paco Buyo record in the 1986-87 La Liga season?

    a. 22

    b. 19

c. 15

d. 10

18. Which keeper played 25 matches in all competitions in 2001-02?

    a. Bodo Illgner
    b. Carlos Sánchez
    c. Albano Bizzarri
    d. César Sánchez

19. How many appearances did Thibaut Courtois make in all competitions in 2019-20?

    a. 30
    b. 38
    c. 43
    d. 50

20. Paco Buyo recorded 20 clean sheets in the 1988-89 La Liga season.

    a. True
    b. False

QUIZ ANSWERS

1. D – Iker Casillas

2. B – False

3. A – 16

4. B – José Vicente Train

5. D – Paco Buyo

6. C – Bodo Illgner

7. A – True

8. B – Kiko Casilla

9. A – 5

10. C – 5th

11. D – Miguel Ángel

12. A – True

13. B – Santiago Cañizares

14. C – 725

15. A – Diego López

16. B – False

17. B – 19

18. D – César Sánchez

19. C – 43

20. B – False

DID YOU KNOW?

1. One of Spain's most famous players during the 1930s was international goalkeeper Ricardo Zamora, who appeared 152 times for Real Madrid between 1930 and 1936. Known as "The Divine One," he helped the club hoist its first two La Liga titles in 1931-32 and 1932-33, with the team going unbeaten for its first title. He signed with Espanyol as a 15-year-old and had earned an Olympic silver medal by the time he was 19 in 1920. Zamora was known for his nerves of steel, reflexes, and charismatic personality. La Liga has a trophy named after him, which is presented to the goalkeeper who concedes the fewest goals per season. He also helped Real win two Copa del Rey trophies.

2. The Ricardo Zamora Trophy was established by a Spanish newspaper called *MARCA* in 1958, to be given to the goalkeeper with the best goals-against average in a league season. When the trophy was first given out, a keeper had to have played a minimum of 15 league matches in the campaign. In 1964, the minimum number of games played was raised to 22, and in 1983, it was raised again, this time, to 28 contests. In addition, a keeper also had to play at least 60 minutes of a game for the contest to count. Even though the award was established in 1958, a list of those who would have won it before that time has been published and released.

3. Real Madrid goalkeepers who have been recognized for earning the Ricardo Zamora Trophy in the Primera División as of 2020 are as follows: 1931-32, Ricardo Zamora; 1932-33, Ricardo Zamora; 1945-46, José Bañón; 1954-55, Juan Alonso; 1960-61, José Vicente Train; 1961-62, José Araquistáin; 1962-63, José Vicente Train; 1963-64, José Vicente Train; 1964-65, Antonio Betancort; 1966-67, Antonio Betancort; 1967-68, Antonio Betancort; 1975-76, Miguel Ángel González; 1982-83, Agustín Rodríguez; 1987-88, Francisco Buyo; 1991-92, Francisco Buyo; 2007-08, Iker Casillas; and 2019-20, Thibaut Courtois.

4. In the 2019-20 La Liga season, Belgian international Thibaut Courtois posted the lowest goals-against average for a Real Madrid goalkeeper to win the Zamora Trophy. He allowed 20 goals in 34 outings for an average of 0.59, which is tied for sixth-best ever in the Primera División for Zamora Trophy winners. It was Courtois's third Zamora award; he also won it with Atlético Madrid in 2012-13 and 2013-14.

5. The first goalkeeper believed to be named full-time captain of Real Madrid was Juanito Alonso, who starred for the first team between 1949 and 1960. Alonso helped the team win 18 trophies, including five straight European Cups between 1956 and 1960 and four La Liga titles. He was also awarded the Ricardo Zamora Trophy in 1954-55. He played nearly 300 games for Los Blancos after learning to play the sport on the beach. Alonso retired due to a broken

collarbone and lung condition and will be remembered as one of the club's greats between the posts.

6. Antonio Betancourt of the Canary Islands played from 1961 to 1971 with the club and took home the Ricardo Zamora Trophy three times, in 1964-65, 1966-67, and 1967-68. Betancourt played 177 official games with the team and helped it win six La Liga titles, a European Cup, and two Copa del Rey trophies. Unfortunately, Betancourt suffered several injuries but often played through them, since goalkeepers couldn't be substituted in his era.

7. Another Real Madrid keeper to take home the Ricardo Zamora Trophy three times was José Vicente Train, who played with the squad from 1960 to 1964 after joining from Espanyol and before leaving for RCD Mallorca. He won the Zamora Trophy for his excellent work in 1960-61, 1962-63, and 1963-64. Vicente Train helped lead the team to the Intercontinental Cup in 1960 as well as four consecutive La Liga titles from 1960-61 to 1963-64 and the Copa del Rey in 1961-62. Nicknamed "The Staple," Vicente Train played 100 times for Real and earned seven caps for Spain.

8. While José Vicente Train helped Real Madrid win four straight La Liga titles between 1961 and 1964, his hopes of winning four consecutive Ricardo Zamora Trophies at the same time were dashed by the play of teammate José Araquistáin in 1961-62. Araquistáin appeared in 25 league games that season and conceded 19 goals to take home the award with a 0.76 goals-against average. He played with Los Blancos from 1961 to 1968 after joining from Real

Sociedad. Araquistáin won six La Liga titles with the side, as well as a Copa del Rey and the 1965-66 European Cup while appearing in 97 official matches and earning six caps for Spain.

9. After joining Real Madrid at the age of nine and playing through the different levels, Iker Casillas made his first-team debut in September 1999. He went on to play 725 official games, a club record for a goalkeeper, before leaving for Porto of Portugal in 2015. The Spanish international wore the captain's armband from 2010 to 2015 and helped the team win 19 trophies, including three European Champions League and five La Liga titles. Casillas was named to the FIFA FIFPro World XI five times, was named best goalkeeper in the world by the IFFHS five times, and also won a Ricardo Zamora Trophy with the team.

10. Iker Casillas may have captured just one Ricardo Zamora Trophy with Real Madrid, but he's one of the club's all-time greats and holds several goalkeeping records for the side. Casillas made the most appearances for any club player in European and international competitions, with most of them coming in the European Champions League. He owns the record for most clean sheets in the tournament and was the youngest keeper to win it when he was 19 years and four days old in 2000. In 2014, Casillas became the second of just three keepers to hoist the trophy as captain, with the others being Peter Schmeichel in 1999 and Manuel Neuer in 2020.

CHAPTER 5:

DARING DEFENDERS

QUIZ TIME!

1. Which defender was shown 11 yellow cards in the 2017-18 La Liga season?

   a. Nacho Fernández
   b. Daniel Carvajal
   c. Marcelo
   d. Theo Hernández

2. As of February 2021, Sergio Ramos had played over 600 games with Madrid.

   a. True
   b. False

3. Which defender earned five assists in the 2015-16 La Liga season?

   a. Danilo
   b. Philipp Lienhart
   c. Álvaro Tejero
   d. Álvaro Arbeloa

4. How many goals did Fernando Hierro score in all competitions in his career with Los Blancos?

   a. 82
   b. 95
   c. 118
   d. 127

5. Which defender posted nine assists in the 2009-10 La Liga season?

   a. Álvaro Arbeloa
   b. Marcelo
   c. Pepe
   d. Marcos Alonso

6. Which defender made 710 appearances in all competitions for the club?

   a. Roberto Carlos
   b. José Antonio Camacho
   c. Manuel Sanchís Jr.
   d. Fernando Hierro

7. Míchel Salgado was the only defender to play in 35 games in the 2004-05 La Liga season.

   a. True
   b. False

8. Who scored three goals in all competitions in 1990-91?

   a. Rafael Gordillo
   b. Miguel Tendillo

c. Víctor Torres Mestre

d. Chucho Solana

9. How many goals did Cicinho score in all competitions in 2005-06?

    a. 8

    b. 5

    c. 3

    d. 0

10. Which defender played 2,773 minutes in the 2010-11 La Liga campaign?

    a. Ricardo Carvalho

    b. Pepe

    c. Raúl Albiol

    d. Nacho Fernández

11. Who netted eight goals in all competitions in 1998-99?

    a. Roberto Carlos

    b. Fernando Sanz

    c. Robert Jarni

    d. Fernando Hierro

12. Manuel Sanchís Jr. holds the club record for the most appearances in all competitions by any player.

    a. True

    b. False

13. Which defender played 3,311 minutes in the 1989-90 La Liga season?

a. Manolo Sanchís
b. Chendo
c. Oscar Ruggeri
d. Rafael Gordillo

14. Who notched six assists across all competitions in 2013-14?

a. Fábio Coentrão
b. Álvaro Arbeloa
c. Pepe
d. Diego Llorente

15. How many goals did Sergio Ramos tally in all competitions in 2018-19?

a. 15
b. 11
c. 6
d. 3

16. Fábio Coentrão was the only defender to be shown a red card in the 2012-13 La Liga season.

a. True
b. False

17. Which defender earned six assists in the 2005-06 La Liga season?

a. Jonathan Woodgate
b. Cicinho
c. Roberto Carlos
d. Carlos Diogo

18. How many times did Sergio Ramos make the FIFPro XI as of 2020?

    a. 6
    b. 13
    c. 8
    d. 11

19. Who scored five goals in the 1985-86 La Liga season?

    a. José Antonio Salguero
    b. Chendo
    c. Antonio Maceda
    d. Isidoro San José

20. Sergio Ramos was shown 18 yellow cards in all competitions in 2013-14.

    a. True
    b. False

QUIZ ANSWERS

1. B – Daniel Carvajal
2. A – True
3. A – Danilo
4. D – 127
5. B – Marcelo
6. C – Manuel Sanchís Jr.
7. B – False
8. B – Miguel Tendillo
9. C – 3
10. A – Ricardo Carvalho
11. D – Fernando Hierro
12. B – False
13. B – Chendo
14. C – Pepe
15. B – 11
16. A – True
17. C – Roberto Carlos
18. D – 11
19. C – Antonio Maceda
20. B – False

DID YOU KNOW?

1. Brazilian international left-back Roberto Carlos combined power and technique for Real Madrid between 1996 and 2007 and was a specialist at free kicks. Carlos was well-known for his long-range shots and had a special knack for scoring from great distances. He may not have hit the net consistently, but, when he did, it was usually something special. He racked up 68 goals in 527 games with the club and helped it win 13 titles, including three European Champions Leagues and four La Liga crowns. Also known for his speed, Carlos's shot was once clocked at 140 kilometers per hour.

2. Right-back Míchel Salgado was known as "Il Due" and played for the club from 1999 to 2009 before being released and signing with the Blackburn Rovers in England. Known for his excellent tackling, the tireless Spanish international helped the team win 11 trophies, including four La Liga and three European Champions Leagues titles. Salgado was a consistent performer who appeared in 371 outings with the team and won the fans over with his commitment and courage.

3. After graduating through the club's youth system, Isidoro San José Pozo played 271 games with the senior side between 1976 and 1986. He was an exquisite defender who joined Real Madrid at the under-12 level and made his first-

team debut at the age of 18. He chipped in with seven goals and helped the squad capture 10 trophies, including four La Liga titles. San José Pozo retired prematurely due to a knee injury but then made a comeback. He also played for the Spanish national side at several age levels and appeared in the 1978 World Cup and the 1976 Olympic Games.

4. Manuel Sanchís Martínez was typically known as "Sanchís" while defending for Real Madrid from 1964 to 1971. He scored just once in his 213 appearances, but his job was to prevent goals, not score them. The Spanish international displayed tremendous physical qualities and skills and was signed from Real Valladolid after a brief spell with Barcelona. Sanchís helped the team win the 1965-66 European Cup as well as four La Liga titles and a Copa del Rey.

5. Arriving on the scene 12 years after his father left, fellow defender Manuel Sanchís Jr. made a significant impact and name for himself at Real Madrid. The former captain spent his entire pro career with the club from 1983 to 2001 and contributed 40 goals in 710 appearances. The legendary Spanish international sweeper debuted with the first team as an 18-year-old in 1983 after developing his skills in the youth system. Sanchís helped the side hoist 21 pieces of silverware, including eight La Liga and two European Champions Leagues titles. He and his father are one of just a few father/son duos to win the European Cup/Champions League.

6. José Antonio Camacho is regarded as one of Real Madrid's top all-time defenders. The legendary Spanish international was known for his will to win and loyalty. The former skipper played 577 official games for the team between 1973 and 1989 after playing for the reserve Castilla side. Camacho suffered a serious knee injury in 1978 that sidelined him for almost two years, but he still managed to help the team haul in 19 trophies, including nine La Liga titles and two UEFA Cups. After retiring, Camacho helped coach the youth teams and became an assistant manager before managing the side himself in two separate stints.

7. After joining Real Madrid from Fluminense in his homeland of Brazil in 2007, Marcelo Vieira da Silva Júnior, simply known as "Marcelo," was still with the side as of February 2021. The Brazilian international left-back has played in over 500 games with the team and has more than 35 goals and 100 assists to his name. Marcelo is one of the most decorated Real Madrid players in history, with a current count of 22 trophies under his belt. These include five La Liga and four Champions League titles. He's also been named to the FIFPro World XI six times and the UEFA Team of the Year three times.

8. From 1931 to 1942, the Real Madrid defense was greatly aided by Spanish international Jacinto Quincoces, who was regarded as one of the best on the globe. However, his career was interrupted between 1936 and 1939 due to the

Spanish Civil War. The team went undefeated in his first season to capture the La Liga title and successfully defended it the next campaign. He also won two Copa del Rey titles with the team. After hanging up his boots, Quincoces managed Real Madrid in two separate stints between 1945 and 1948. He also managed several other clubs, including a brief stint with the Spanish national side.

9. Born in Uruguay, José Emilio Santamaría played internationally for both his homeland and Spain and solidified the Real Madrid back line between 1957 and 1966. Known as "The Wall," due to his aerial skills and tackling ability, he helped the team capture 11 trophies, including five La Liga titles and four European Cups. He made 337 official appearances with the side, and, after his playing days, Santamaría turned to football management. He was in charge of the Spanish national side between 1980 and 1982.

10. As of February 2021, Sergio Ramos was still wearing the armband for Real Madrid after being appointed skipper in 2015. He joined the club from Sevilla in 2005 and is considered by many to be its best defender ever. The Spanish international displays brilliant heading and defensive abilities combined with exceptional leadership skills. Ramos has helped Los Blancos capture 22 trophies, including five La Liga and four European Champions League titles. He's also earned numerous individual

accolades, such as being named to the FIFPro World XI 11 times. Ramos has played over 660 games with the team, scoring 100 goals, and he is currently the most-capped Spanish international with 178 appearances.

CHAPTER 6:

MAESTROS OF THE MIDFIELD

QUIZ TIME!

1. Which midfielder posted eight assists in the 2019-20 La Liga season?

    a. Casemiro
    b. Federico Valverde
    c. Luka Modrić
    d. Toni Kroos

2. Pirri made 561 career appearances in all competitions for Madrid.

    a. True
    b. False

3. Which midfielder earned eight assists in the 2000-01 La Liga season?

    a. Guti
    b. Steve McManaman
    c. Njitap Geremi
    d. Claude Makélélé

4. Who scored seven goals in all competitions in 1997-98?

   a. Christian Karembeu
   b. José Amavisca
   c. Clarence Seedorf
   d. Jaime

5. How many assists did Mesut Özil record in all competitions in 2012-13?

   a. 24
   b. 18
   c. 15
   d. 11

6. Which midfielder notched seven assists in the 2008-09 La Liga campaign?

   a. Fernando Gago
   b. Royston Drenthe
   c. Dani Parejo
   d. Rubén de la Red

7. Mateo Kovačić was the only midfielder to be shown a red card in the 2015-16 La Liga season.

   a. True
   b. False

8. Which player tallied six goals in the 1993-94 La Liga season?

   a. Santi Aragón
   b. Villarroya

c. Alberto Toril

d. Robert Prosinecki

9. How many assists did David Beckham earn in the 2005-06 La Liga season?

   a. 4
   b. 7
   c. 11
   d. 15

10. Which midfielder scored 13 goals in all competitions in 1992-93?

    a. Robert Prosinecki
    b. Luis Milla
    c. Míchel
    d. Luis Enrique

11. In what season was Toni Kroos first named to the UEFA La Liga Team of the Season?

    a. 2014-15
    b. 2016-17
    c. 2018-19
    d. 2019-20

12. Luka Modrić's 30 La Liga matches were the most by a Madrid player in the 2014-15 La Liga season.

    a. True
    b. False

13. Which Italian team did Clarence Seedorf join Los Blancos from in 1996?

    a. Inter Milan

    b. Juventus

    c. Sampdoria

    d. Roma

14. Which player was shown seven yellow cards in the 2002-03 La Liga season?

    a. Albert Celades

    b. Santiago Solari

    c. Claude Makélélé

    d. Flávio Conceição

15. How many goals did David Beckham score across all competitions in his 159 matches with Madrid?

    a. 20

    b. 13

    c. 12

    d. 10

16. Midfielder Míchel scored nine goals in the 1995-96 La Liga season.

    a. True

    b. False

17. Who scored 13 goals in all competitions in 2002-03?

    a. Steve McManaman

    b. Guti

c. Santiago Solari

d. Flávio Conceição

18. Which player was named UEFA Club Footballer of the Year for 1999-2000?

    a. Achraf Hakimi

    b. Raymond Kopa

    c. Mateo Kovačić

    d. Fernando Redondo

19. How many goals did Pirri score in all competitions in his career with Madrid?

    a. 34

    b. 78

    c. 130

    d. 172

20. Casemiro was shown 13 yellow cards across all competitions in 2017-18.

    a. True

    b. False

QUIZ ANSWERS

1. C – Luka Modrić

2. A – True

3. B – Steve McManaman

4. C – Clarence Seedorf

5. A – 24

6. A – Fernando Gago

7. A – True

8. D – Robert Prosinecki

9. C – 11

10. C – Míchel

11. B – 2016-17

12. B – False

13. C – Sampdoria

14. C – Claude Makélélé

15. A – 20

16. B – False

17. B – Guti

18. D – Fernando Redondo

19. D – 172

20. A – True

DID YOU KNOW?

1. Former Real Madrid captain Fernando Hierro was a versatile player who served as a center-back and defensive midfielder for the team between 1989 and 2003 and was its assistant manager in 2014-15. He played in 601 contests with the squad and contributed offensively with 127 goals while helping his teammates hoist 16 pieces of silverware, including five La Liga titles and three European Champions League crowns. The Spanish international had two older brothers, Manuel and Antonio, who were also professional footballers.

2. French international Zinedine Zidane, who was still managing Real Madrid as of February 2021, is a club icon. Known as "Zizou," he joined the club from Juventus in 2001 after winning the Ballon d'Or there in 1998. He quickly became one of the side's most effective and popular players due to his passing, creativity, and ball control. Zidane remained until 2006 and tallied 49 goals in 227 outings while helping the team capture six trophies, including a European Champions League and La Liga title. Zidane netted the decisive goal in the 2002 Champions League final against Bayer Leverkusen.

3. Raymond Kopa arrived from Stade de Reims in 1956 and left Real Madrid to return to the same French club in 1959. In between, he helped the Spanish side hoist two La Liga

and three straight European Cup titles, along with a Latin Cup. He also won the Ballon d'Or in 1958. The French international, known as "Little Napoleon," was famous for his dribbling skills, immaculate crosses, and playmaking abilities. He notched 30 goals in 103 contests with Real. In 2018, the Kopa Trophy was established in France to be awarded to the best under-21 player in the world. The first recipient was Kylian Mbappé.

4. After a stellar stint with Bayern Munich from 2007 to 2014, international Toni Kroos joined Real Madrid for an estimated €30 million as the ninth German player to sign with the squad. He was still with the club as of February 2021, and he has solidified his standing as one of the side's best midfielders ever after playing over 300 games with the outfit. Kroos has helped his teammates lift 13 trophies, including three straight European Champions League and two La Liga titles. He's also received several individual awards, such as being named to the UEFA La Liga Team of the Season for 2016-17 and 2019-20.

5. Dutch international Clarence Seedorf wasn't with Real Madrid for long; he joined from Sampdoria in 1996 and returned to the Italian Serie A to play with Inter Milan in 2000. He was quite successful, though, as he helped the club hoist four trophies, including La Liga and European Champions League crowns. The powerful midfielder was a key player for Los Blancos, and when he retired in 2014 to enter football management, he had four Champions

League medals around his neck from three different clubs. Two of these came with AC Milan while the others were won with Real Madrid and Ajax.

6. Fernando Redondo was an Argentine international who arrived in Madrid in 1994 from Tenerife in the Canary Islands after beginning his career in his homeland. Redondo was at his best with Real Madrid and assisted the team in winning two La Liga titles, two European Champions League crowns, a Supercopa de España, and an Intercontinental Cup. He was nicknamed "The Prince" and known for his playmaking while chipping in with five goals in 228 matches. Redondo was named Real Madrid Player of the Year for 1996-97 and 1999-2000 and the UEFA Club Footballer of the Year for 1999-2000 before leaving for AC Milan in 2000.

7. Spanish international Xabi Alonso, who was nicknamed "La Barba Roja" (The Red Beard), left Liverpool for Los Blancos in 2009 after proving he was one of the best technical central midfielders in the world. He was classy and elegant and helped his new teammates hoist half a dozen trophies, including La Liga and European Champions League titles. Alonso joined the squad around the same time as Kaká and Cristiano Ronaldo and contributed six goals in 236 games. He left the side in 2014 for Bayern Munich and later returned to Real Madrid to take a youth team coaching role.

8. German international hard man Uli Stielike enforced his

will in the Real Madrid midfield from 1977 to 1985 after arriving from Borussia Mönchengladbach. Known for his commitment, creativity, tackling, and positioning, the combative player helped the club win six titles, including a UEFA Cup and three La Liga championships. This came after winning three Bundesliga titles, a German Cup, and a UEFA Cup in his homeland. Legend has it that Real Madrid president Santiago Bernabéu traveled to Germany to sign Borussia player Herbert Wimmer but signed Stielike instead after seeing him play. Stielike could also play as a sweeper and contributed 50 goals in 308 contests with Real.

9. Known as one of the greatest players of his generation, former England captain David Beckham spent 2003 to 2007 with Real Madrid and netted 20 goals in 159 outings. Beckham was as well-known off the pitch as on it and displayed excellent playmaking abilities and a free-kick technique that resulted in some stunning goals. A key voice in the dressing room, the hard-working midfielder inspired his Los Blancos teammates to a La Liga title and a Supercopa de España triumph. Beckham won numerous team and individual awards during his career with Manchester United, the LA Galaxy, AC Milan, and Paris Saint-Germain, including the Real Madrid Player of the Year honor for 2005-06.

10. Playing with Real Madrid from 1999 to 2003, before David Beckham arrived, was another high-profile English

international midfielder, Steve McManaman. He joined from his hometown club of Liverpool and quickly won over the team's followers with his easy-going personality, versatility, hard work, and unselfish play. He scored a crucial goal in May 2000 to help Los Blancos win the European Champions League and would win it again two years later. McManaman also helped the side capture two La Liga titles and three other trophies. He notched 14 goals in 158 matches before leaving for Manchester City.

CHAPTER 7:
SENSATIONAL STRIKERS & FORWARDS

QUIZ TIME!

1. How many goals did Karim Benzema score in the 2019-20 La Liga season?

   a. 13
   b. 18
   c. 21
   d. 25

2. Raúl is the club's leader in appearances in all competitions as of the end of 2020.

   a. True
   b. False

3. Who recorded 16 assists in all competitions in 2017-18?

   a. Isco
   b. Marco Asensio
   c. Lucas Vázquez
   d. Cristiano Ronaldo

4. Which forward scored 21 goals in the 2004-05 La Liga season?

   a. Javier Portillo
   b. Zinedine Zidane
   c. Michael Owen
   d. Ronaldo Luís Nazário

5. Who scored 28 La Liga goals in the 1994-95 season?

   a. Raúl
   b. Iván Zamorano
   c. Michael Laudrup
   d. Alfonso

6. How many goals did Gareth Bale score in the 2018-19 La Liga season?

   a. 8
   b. 12
   c. 5
   d. 14

7. Cristiano Ronaldo played in 300 La Liga matches with Real Madrid.

   a. True
   b. False

8. Which forward netted 20 goals in all competitions in 1988-89?

   a. Alberto Aguilà
   b. Bernd Shuster

c. Rafael Martin Vázquez

d. Emilio Butragueño

9. Which forward joined Real Madrid from Arsenal of the English Premier League?

   a. Michael Owen

   b. Gareth Bale

   c. Nicolas Anelka

   d. Arjen Robben

10. Which forward scored 14 goals in the 1996-97 La Liga season?

    a. Irurzun

    b. Dejan Petkovic

    c. Predrag Mijatović

    d. Víctor Sánchez

11. Which forward earned 12 assists in the 2003-04 La Liga season?

    a. Zinedine Zidane

    b. Luís Figo

    c. Ronaldo Luís Nazário

    d. Antonio Núñez

12. Arjen Robben was shown 13 yellow cards in the 2008-09 La Liga campaign.

    a. True

    b. False

13. Which player won the La Liga Golden Boot in 2003-04?

    a. Kaká
    b. Ronaldo Luís Nazário
    c. Fernando Morientes
    d. Gonzalo Higuaín

14. Which forward scored 19 goals in all competitions in 1999-2000?

    a. Perica Ognjenović
    b. Rolando Zárate
    c. Sávio
    d. Fernando Morientes

15. Who contributed 13 goals in the 2014-15 La Liga season?

    a. James Rodríguez
    b. Isco
    c. Jesé
    d. Chicharito

16. Real Madrid had four players with 10 or more goals in the 2011-12 La Liga season.

    a. True
    b. False

17. How many goals did Gareth Bale score in the 2013-14 La Liga season?

    a. 10
    b. 12
    c. 15
    d. 20

18. How many goals did Jorge Valdano score in the 1986-87 La Liga season?

    a. 11
    b. 7
    c. 4
    d. 2

19. Who tallied 11 goals in the 2016-17 La Liga season?

    a. Isco
    b. Gareth Bale
    c. James Rodríguez
    d. Karim Benzema

20. Ángel Di María recorded 17 assists in the 2013-14 La Liga season.

    a. True
    b. False

QUIZ ANSWERS

1. C – 21

2. A – True

3. C – Lucas Vázquez

4. D – Ronaldo Luís Nazário

5. B – Iván Zamorano

6. A – 8

7. B – False

8. D – Emilio Butragueño

9. C – Nicolas Anelka

10. C – Predrag Mijatović

11. A – Zinedine Zidane

12. B – False

13. B – Ronaldo Luís Nazário

14. D – Fernando Morientes

15. A – James Rodríguez

16. B – False

17. C – 15

18. B – 7

19. D – Karim Benzema

20. A – True

DID YOU KNOW?

1. Dutch international winger Arjen Robben arrived at Real Madrid from Chelsea in August 2007. His stay was brief, though: He played just two seasons after inking a five-year deal and costing the club a reported €35 million. He notched 13 goals in 65 games and helped it win the La Liga title in his first season and the Supercopa de España in 2008. When Florentino Pérez became club president and Cristiano Ronaldo and Kaká were signed, Robben's services weren't as essential anymore. He was sold to Bayern Munich for approximately €25 million in 2009 and claimed he was forced to leave the team. After leaving Los Blancos, he won 20 trophies and several individual awards with Bayern Munich.

2. After he notched 28 goals in 90 games with Arsenal, Real Madrid paid the English club €35 million for forward Nikolas Anelka in the summer of 1999. The French international was a consistent scorer but not a prolific one. He often had difficulty getting along with teammates and that could explain why he played for a dozen different clubs during his pro career. Anelka played just 33 times for Real Madrid and netted seven goals while helping win the European Champions League. He was then sold to Paris Saint-Germain just 12 months after arriving. The French side paid a reported €34.5 million for Anelka, enabling Real Madrid to recoup most of its money.

3. Striker Álvaro Morata joined Real Madrid in 2008 and competed mainly for the club's youth side and B team between 2010 and 2013, scoring 11 goals in 52 games with the senior side. He was then sold to Juventus in 2014 for €20 million. While in Italy, Morata won two league titles and Coppa Italia championships. Real Madrid then decided they wanted him back and used their buy-back option to reacquire him for €30 million. Morata notched 20 goals in 43 matches in 2016-17, but Real Madrid then sold him to Chelsea for €66 million. He helped Los Blancos win eight trophies, including two La Liga and European Champions League titles.

4. Michael Owen was another world-class finisher who had a brief stint with Real Madrid. The English international and 2001 Ballon d'Or winner notched 16 goals in 45 competitive matches after joining from Liverpool in the summer of 2004. His one-on-one skills, speed, and attacking ability made him a fan favorite while playing alongside fellow stars such as Raúl, Luís Figo, Zinedine Zidane, David Beckham, and Ronaldo in the club's Galácticos era. After a slow start, Owen finished the 2004-05 campaign with 13 La Liga goals and posted the highest ratio of goals scored to the number of minutes played in the league. However, he left for Newcastle United in August 2005 after a trophy-less season in Spain.

5. As of February 2021, Real Madrid's most expensive transfer fee was dished out to Chelsea for Belgian international

winger and captain Eden Hazard. Costing €115 million, he joined in June 2019 and signed a contract lasting until June 2024. He asked Luka Modrić if he could wear number 10 but was turned down, and he was then given the famous number 7, which was formerly worn by team legends Raúl González, Emilio Butragueño, and Cristiano Ronaldo. Hazard played only 16 La Liga games and 22 overall in his first Los Blancos season due to injuries and tallied just one goal. However, the team was still crowned league champions in the Covid-19-interrupted campaign.

6. Winger Gareth Bale didn't come cheap, either: Real Madrid splashed out a then world-record €101 million to Tottenham Hotspur for his services in September 2013. Since then, the Welsh international has helped the side capture 13 trophies, including four European Champions League and two La Liga titles. He has chipped in with just over 100 goals in 251 games. Bale's time in Madrid has been hampered by injuries, but he's also scored many crucial goals for the team, resulting in several pieces of silverware. His relationship with the club soured, though, and he was sent back to Tottenham in September 2020 on a year-long loan.

7. Brazilian international striker Ronaldo Luís Nazário de Lima, otherwise known as "Ronaldo," had already established himself as one of the world's greatest players and won numerous individual honors by the time he arrived at Real Madrid in 2002. The goal-scoring

phenomenon tallied 104 times in 177 games for the club and helped it hoist two La Liga titles and two other trophies. The two-time Ballon d'Or award winner (1997 and 2002) scored in his Los Blancos debut and continued to thrill supporters with sensational performances thereafter. Ronaldo won the La Liga Golden Boot in 2003-04 with 21 goals and bade farewell in 2007, when he joined AC Milan.

8. Fernando Morientes played with Real Madrid from 1997 to 2005, appearing in 242 games and contributing 91 goals. The Spanish international formed a lethal partnership with Raúl and helped the team win three European Champions League and two La Liga titles along with six other trophies. Morientes was great in the air, but the old-fashioned center-forward's playing time was reduced with the arrival of Ronaldo. Morientes was loaned in 2003-04 to Monaco, where he excelled by being named the UEFA Club Forward of the Year, the UEFA Champions League top scorer, and a member of the Ligue 1 Team of the Year. He was then sold to Liverpool in January 2005 for a reported €9.3 million.

9. Former club captain Amancio Amaro Varela, who was known simply as "Amancio," proved to be one of the best forwards in team history. Between 1962 and 1976, the right-winger notched 155 goals and exhibited fabulous skills and pace while helping the side win 13 trophies, including nine La Liga titles and the 1965-66 European

Cup. Amancio also shared the La Liga Golden Boot in 1968-69 and 1969-70. After hanging up his boots, he became manager of Real Madrid's reserve team and then the first-team squad and was elected to the board of directors.

10. Known as "Juanito," Juan Gómez González racked up 121 goals for Real Madrid between 1977 and 1987 as one of the team's legendary forwards. Famous for his fiery temper, passion, and skill, he was a player who had a hard time accepting defeat, and this endeared him to the club's fans. The Spanish international won 10 trophies with the club total, including five La Liga crowns and a pair of UEFA Cups. Juanito shared the La Liga Golden Boot in 1983-84 with 17 goals and sadly passed away in 1992 after being involved in a traffic accident while on his way home from watching his beloved Real Madrid play.

CHAPTER 8:

NOTABLE TRANSFERS & SIGNINGS

QUIZ TIME!

1. Which player was sold by Real Madrid for a club-record fee (as of February 2021)?

   a. Ángel Di María
   b. Cristiano Ronaldo
   c. Mesut Özil
   d. Álvaro Morata

2. Real Madrid acquired goalkeeper Ricardo Zamora for the approximate equivalent of €900 in 1930.

   a. True
   b. False

3. Which player did Madrid acquire from Eintracht Frankfurt for a reported €63 million in 2019-20?

   a. Reinier
   b. Rodrygo

c. Ferland Mendy

d. Luka Jović

4. What was the transfer fee Los Blancos received when selling Cristiano Ronaldo?

    a. €117 million

    b. €134 million

    c. €150 million

    d. €210 million

5. From which club did Real acquire Ronaldo Luís Nazário in 2002-03?

    a. AC Milan

    b. Cruzeiro EC

    c. Inter Milan

    d. PSV Eindhoven

6. Which club was Claude Makélélé sold to in 2003-04?

    a. Paris Saint-Germain

    b. Chelsea FC

    c. Olympique Marseille

    d. Celta de Vigo

7. Sergio Ramos was acquired from Santos FC for €20 million in 2005-06.

    a. True

    b. False

8. Who was signed for €35 million in 1999-2000 from Arsenal FC?

a. Christian Karembeu

b. Perica Ognjenović

c. Nicolas Anelka

d. Elvir Baljić

9. How much did Real pay to sign Zinedine Zidane?

   a. €82.70 million

   b. €77.50 million

   c. €62 million

   d. €55 million

10. From which Premier League club did Madrid sign Cristiano Ronaldo?

    a. Liverpool FC

    b. Manchester City

    c. Arsenal FC

    d. Manchester United

11. Which player did Madrid sign from FC Barcelona in 2000-01?

    a. Pedro Munitis

    b. Luís Figo

    c. Flávio Conceição

    d. César Sánchez

12. In 1995-96, Michael Laudrup was acquired from FC Barcelona for a fee of €9.60 million.

    a. True

    b. False

13. What was the transfer fee that the club paid Chelsea FC for Eden Hazard in 2019-20?

    a. €115 million
    b. €110 million
    c. €105.5 million
    d. €94 million

14. Which club was Danilo signed from in 2015-16?

    a. RCD Mallorca
    b. Sevilla FC
    c. S.L. Benfica
    d. FC Porto

15. How much was the transfer fee paid to acquire Gareth Bale from Tottenham Hotspur in 2013-14?

    a. €71.25 million
    b. €84.75 million
    c. €101 million
    d. €115 million

16. Real Madrid acquired Zinedine Zidane from Juventus in 2001-02.

    a. True
    b. False

17. Los Blancos transferred Gonzalo Higuaín to which Italian club for a fee of €39 million?

    a. SSC Napoli
    b. Torino FC

c. FC Crotone

d. ACF Fiorentina

18. What was the transfer fee paid to acquire Cristiano Ronaldo in 2009-10?

   a. €63 million

   b. €75 million

   c. €85 million

   d. €94 million

19. Which French club was Karim Benzema signed from in 2009-10?

   a. Stade de Reims

   b. OGC Nice

   c. Olympique Lyon

   d. Dijon FCO

20. The team paid a transfer fee of €50 million to acquire David Beckham from Manchester United.

   a. True

   b. False

QUIZ ANSWERS

1. B – Cristiano Ronaldo

2. A – True

3. D – Luka Jović

4. A – €117 million

5. C – Inter Milan

6. B – Chelsea FC

7. B – False

8. C – Nicolas Anelka

9. B – €77.50 million

10. D – Manchester United

11. B – Luís Figo

12. A – True

13. A – €115 million

14. D – FC Porto

15. C – €101 million

16. A – True

17. A – SSC Napoli

18. D – €94 million

19. C – Olympique Lyon

20. B – False

DID YOU KNOW?

1. The five most expensive transfer fees reportedly paid by Real Madrid as of February 2021 are: winger Eden Hazard from Chelsea FC for €115 million in 2019-20; winger Gareth Bale from Tottenham Hotspur for €101 million in 2013-14; winger Cristiano Ronaldo from Manchester United for €94 million in 2009-10; midfielder Zinedine Zidane from Juventus FC for €77.5 million in 2001-02; and midfielder James Rodríguez from AS Monaco for €75 million in 2014-15.

2. The five highest transfer fees reportedly received for players by Real Madrid are: winger Cristiano Ronaldo to Juventus FC for €117 million in 2018-19; winger Ángel Di María to Manchester United for €75 million in 2014-15; forward Álvaro Morata to Chelsea FC for €66 million in 2017-18; midfielder Mesut Özil to Arsenal FC for €47 million in 2013-14; and midfielder Mateo Kovačić to Chelsea FC for €45 million in 2019-20.

3. Argentine international defender Gabriel Heinze generally under-performed at Manchester United and eventually lost his starting job. He wanted to move to Liverpool in 2007, but manager Sir Alex Ferguson had no intention of selling him to his club's fiercest rivals. The transfer saga dragged on and was finally settled by a tribunal board that ruled Man United didn't have to cave in to the player's

demands. Ferguson then shipped Heinze to Real Madrid instead for approximately €12 million. Heinze played just 60 games with the club and helped it win the La Liga in 2007-08 and Supercopa de España in 2008 before joining Marseille in July 2009 even though he had signed for four years with Real.

4. Croatian international midfielder Luka Modrić tried to force a move to Chelsea in 2011 even though he had signed a six-year contract with Tottenham Hotspur in 2010. Spurs rejected three Chelsea bids for the player, although Modrić claimed they agreed to sell him if a bigger club wanted him. Modrić refused to play in the 2011-12 season opener but changed his plans when being told he wouldn't be paid if he walked out. Modrić played the season with Tottenham but sat out the 2012-13 preseason to force a move. The club fined him £80,000 and sold him to Real Madrid for €10 million, which was approximately €12 million less than Chelsea's offer a year earlier.

5. Because Tottenham Hotspur didn't want to sell Luka Modrić to a fellow English Premier League club, they sent him to Real Madrid instead. Since arriving in 2012, he has proved himself to be a world-class player and has helped the side win 16 trophies. These include two La Liga and four European Champions League titles, three UEFA Super Cups and Supercopa de España, a Copa del Rey, and three straight FIFA Club World Cups. Modrić was still with Los Blancos as of February 2021 and had played close

to 200 games with the team while also winning several individual awards.

6. Some Real Madrid fans were startled when the club signed English defender Jonathan Woodgate from Newcastle United for €18.3 million in the summer of 2004. Woodgate had a history of being injury-prone and didn't dress for a single contest in his first season in Madrid. He finally made his debut in 2005 and marked the occasion by scoring an own goal and being ejected after receiving two yellow cards. Woodgate played a total of 14 games for the club in three years and was sold to Middlesbrough for a reported €9.6 million in 2007. His signing by Real was named the worst transfer of the twenty-first century by the Spanish newspaper *MARCA*.

7. Spanish international midfielder Juan Mata joined Real Madrid when he was 15 but didn't really graduate past the club's reserve side and was sold to Valencia in 2007. He helped them win the Copa del Rey while scoring 46 goals and was then sold to Chelsea in 2011 where he added another 33 goals and helped the side win an FA Cup, Europa League, and European Champions League title. He was also voted the team's player of the year two seasons in a row. Mata joined Manchester United in January 2014 and has helped the side win four trophies and chipped in with 50 goals while still playing with the team as of February 2021.

8. Goalkeeper Santiago Cañizares spent his youth career with Real Madrid and played with the C and B teams.

However, he was sent out on loan from 1990 to 1992 before playing a game for the senior side and then joined Celta de Vigo. Cañizares performed so well that Los Blancos reacquired the Spanish international in 1994. He left again in 1998, though, when he joined Valencia. While there, he became team captain and led his side to seven trophies and a pair of European Champions League finals. He also shared the Ricardo Zamora Trophy in 1992-93 and won it in 2000-01, 2001-02, and 2003-04 while being named to the UEFA Team of the Year in 2001.

9. Argentine international midfielder Esteban Cambiasso also started in Real Madrid's youth system and reserve team. He then returned to his homeland in 1998 and re-joined Los Blancos in 2002. However, he was mainly a substitute when the team won the La Liga in 2002-03. He left the club again in 2004 and joined Inter Milan on a free transfer after appearing in 65 games with Real and winning four trophies. Cambiasso suddenly flourished and helped his new team win 15 trophies, including five straight league titles and a European Champions League. He joined Leicester City in 2014 and was voted player of the year in his first season. Cambiasso won two league titles in Greece with Olympiacos before retiring at the age of 37 with 22 winner's medals to his name.

10. Real Madrid didn't have much luck with another Argentine international, center-back Walter Samuel, either. He was acquired in 2004 from Roma of Italy for a reported fee of €25 million. The club didn't get a good return for its

money; Samuel played one season and 40 games with the team before he was sold to Inter Milan for €16 million in 2005. Like his teammate Esteban Cambiasso, Samuel then became one of Inter's most dependable players and helped the side win 13 trophies, including five consecutive league titles and a European Champions League. He joined Swiss club Basel in 2014 and won two straight league titles before retiring at the age of 39.

CHAPTER 9:

ODDS & ENDS

QUIZ TIME!

1. Real Madrid was the first Spanish club to do what with their kits?

    a. Display advertising
    b. Wear an alternate jersey
    c. Display player names on the backs of their jerseys
    d. Display numbers on the backs of their jerseys

2. For one season in the 1920s, the team wore black shorts but abandoned the look after one season, claiming the shorts brought bad luck.

    a. True
    b. False

3. How many matches did the team win in its first La Liga season?

    a. 4
    b. 10

c. 11

d. 15

4. Which side did Los Blancos hammer 11-2 for the club's record La Liga victory in 1959-60?

a. Granada CF

b. Atlético Madrid

c. Elche CF

d. Real Sociedad

5. Who was the youngest player to make an appearance for the squad as of 2020 at the age of 16 years and 157 days?

a. Lasada

b. Martin Ødegaard

c. Raúl

d. Alberto Rivera

6. Who was the first Real Madrid player to win the Ballon d'Or in 1957?

a. Raymond Kopa

b. Alfredo Di Stéfano

c. Ferenc Puskás

d. Joseíto

7. Real Madrid has never been relegated as of 2020.

a. True

b. False

8. Which player scored the fastest goal in team history in the 1994-95 La Liga match against Sevilla FC?

a. Luis Enrique

b. Emilio Butragueño

c. Raúl

d. Iván Zamorano

9. Madrid's biggest La Liga defeat was an 8-1 thumping by which club in 1929-30?

a. Cádiz CF

b. Athletic Bilbao

c. RCD Espanyol

d. FC Barcelona

10. What is the name of the local derby between Real Madrid and Atlético Madrid?

a. El Madrileño Clásico

b. Los Clásico

c. El Derbi Madrileño

d. Los Derbi

11. How many times did Cristiano Ronaldo win the Ballon d'Or with Madrid?

a. 6

b. 4

c. 2

d. 1

12. The fastest goal scored by a Real player was 13 seconds.

a. True

b. False

13. Who was the club's first manager to win the Best FIFA Football Coach award?

   a. Carlo Ancelotti
   b. Vicente del Bosque
   c. Zinedine Zidane
   d. José Mourinho

14. How many La Liga matches did the team win in 2011-12?

   a. 32
   b. 39
   c. 25
   d. 22

15. Madrid demolished which team 9-0 for a club-record victory in a European Cup match?

   a. Sporting CP
   b. FC Nürnberg
   c. Górnik Zabrze
   d. Boldklubben 1913

16. Six Real Madrid players won the 2010 FIFA World Cup with Spain.

   a. True
   b. False

17. Who was the oldest player to make a La Liga appearance for the team, at the age of 38 years and 231 days?

   a. Ferenc Puskás
   b. Paco Buyo

c. Alfredo Di Stéfano

d. Paco Gento

18. Which player scored a hat-trick in eight minutes in a La Liga match against Granada CF in 2014-15?

    a. Gareth Bale
    b. Cristiano Ronaldo
    c. Karim Benzema
    d. Toni Kroos

19. How many La Liga matches did the squad draw in 1978-79?

    a. 9
    b. 12
    c. 15
    d. 17

20. The most games the club has won in a La Liga season as of 2020 is 34.

    a. True
    b. False

QUIZ ANSWERS

1. D – Display numbers on the backs of their jerseys

2. A – True

3. C – 11

4. C – Elche CF

5. B – Martin Ødegaard

6. B – Alfredo Di Stéfano

7. A – True

8. D – Iván Zamorano

9. C – RCD Espanyol

10. C – El Derbi Madrileño

11. B – 4

12. A – True

13. C – Zinedine Zidane

14. A – 32

15. D – Boldklubben 1913

16. B – False

17. A – Ferenc Puskás

18. B – Cristiano Ronaldo

19. C – 15

20. B – False

DID YOU KNOW?

1. Real Madrid typically plays its home games at the Estadio Santiago Bernabéu in the city of Madrid, Spain. The ground has a capacity of 81,044 and is the largest in Madrid and second-largest in the nation behind Camp Nou of Barcelona. The stadium was originally known as Estadio Real Madrid Club de Fútbol from its opening in 1947 until 1955 and is commonly known as the Bernabéu.

2. The record attendance at the Bernabéu Stadium was 129,690 for the Real Madrid versus AC Milan contest on April 19, 1956. The venue was constructed from October 1944 to December 1947 and officially opened on December 14, 1947. The stadium was renovated in 1982, 2001, and 2020; work was still going on in February 2021. It was expanded in 1953, 1992, 1994, and 2011.

3. The club moved to the multi-purpose Campo de O'Donnell ground in 1912 to play its home games and remained there for 11 years. The side then played at Campo de Ciudad Lineal for a year with its capacity of 8,000. The next move was in 1923 to Estadio Chamartín, which could hold 22,500 fans. However, as the team's popularity soared, the Santiago Bernabéu Stadium was built to accommodate the ever-growing number of supporters.

4. Real Madrid Castilla Club de Fútbol is a Spanish soccer team that was competing in the Segunda División B –

Group 1 in 2020-21. This is Real Madrid's reserve team, which competes in the same league system as the senior squad. However, reserve teams for Spanish clubs are not allowed to play in the same division as the club's first team. This rule means Real Madrid Castilla is ineligible to earn promotion to the La Liga Primera División. In addition, reserve teams aren't permitted to compete in the annual Copa del Rey tournament.

5. Real Madrid moved its home contests to the 6,000-capacity Estadio Alfredo Di Stéfano in Madrid in June 2020 due to the Covid-19 pandemic and the fact the Bernabéu was under renovation. Built and opened in 2006, the Estadio Alfredo Di Stéfano is a multi-purpose venue that was named after former Real Madrid soccer legend Alfredo Di Stéfano. The stadium has also been the home ground for the reserve Real Madrid Castilla team since 2006 and is part of the Ciudad Real Madrid training facilities.

6. Since the club's inception in 1902, the squad has traditionally worn an all-white kit at home. However, the team wore black shorts for one season in the 1920s but quickly discarded the experiment after several poor results. In November 1947, in a match against Atlético Madrid, Real Madrid became the first Spanish soccer team to wear numbers on their shirts. The team's traditional away colors are all purple or all blue, but the squad has worn several other color combinations over the years such as black, orange, red, and green.

7. The Spanish word "real" translates to "royal" in English and was bestowed upon the club in 1920 by King Alfonso XIII along with the royal crown in the emblem. Unlike most sports organizations around the world, which are privately owned, Real Madrid has always been owned and operated by members, known as socios, since the club's inception. The club record is one of the most valuable in the world and is also typically one of the highest-earning sports clubs annually.

8. Real Madrid is one of just three founding members of La Liga that has never been relegated from the Primera División since its inaugural season in 1929. The other two are Athletic Bilbao and Barcelona. The club's biggest soccer rivalries are against Barcelona, with the fixture being known as "El Clásico," and against neighbors Atlético Madrid, with the contests being known as "El Derbi Madrileño."

9. In December 2000, Real Madrid was named the FIFA Club of the 20th Century in a worldwide poll. The club earned 42.35% of the vote and was awarded the FIFA Centennial Order of Merit in May 2004. In addition, the organization was named the Best European Club of the 20th Century by the IFFHS (International Federation of Football History and Statistics).

10. The club operates its own broadcasting venture, Real Madrid TV. This is an encrypted digital television channel broadcast in Spanish and English that specializes in club

news and events. The head offices are located at the training center Ciudad Real Madrid. The club also publishes a magazine called *Hala Madrid* four times per year for its members and Madridistas Fan Club cardholders. Hala Madrid, translated to English is "Forward Madrid" or "Go Madrid," which is also the name of the club's official anthem.

CHAPTER 10:

DOMESTIC COMPETITION

QUIZ TIME!

1. What year did Real Madrid win its first Copa del Rey?

    a. 1934

    b. 1917

    c. 1905

    d. 1903

2. Real Madrid holds the record for the most La Liga titles won as of 2020.

    a. True

    b. False

3. Which club did Los Blancos defeat in the 1986 Copa de La Liga?

    a. FC Barcelona

    b. Real Betis

    c. Sevilla FC

    d. Atlético Madrid

4. How many times has Real won the Supercopa de España as of 2020?

    a. 8
    b. 11
    c. 14
    d. 16

5. Madrid defeated which club 6-5 on aggregate to win the 2008 Supercopa de España?

    a. Villarreal CF
    b. Valencia CF
    c. Elche CF
    d. FC Barcelona

6. Which side did Madrid beat in the 1973-74 Copa del Rey final?

    a. Real Sociedad
    b. SD Ibiza
    c. Castilla CF
    d. Athletic Bilbao

7. Real Madrid has won the La Liga title for consecutive seasons on two separate occasions.

    a. True
    b. False

8. As of 2020, how many times has Real Madrid captured the La Liga title?

    a. 24
    b. 29

c. 34

d. 40

9. Which team did the club humble in the 2003 Supercopa de España?

    a. RCD Mallorca
    b. FC Barcelona
    c. Real Valladolid
    d. SD Huesca

10. Madrid downed which club in the 1979-80 Copa del Rey final?

    a. Real Madrid Castilla
    b. CD Castellón
    c. Celta de Vigo
    d. RCD Español

11. How many times did Real Madrid win the Madrid Regional Championship?

    a. 6
    b. 12
    c. 17
    d. 23

12. Real Madrid was the last club ever to win the Copa de Liga in 1986.

    a. True
    b. False

13. Madrid defeated which team to hoist the 1992-93 Copa del Rey?

    a. Real Valladolid
    b. Sporting de Gijón
    c. Real Zaragoza
    d. FC Barcelona

14. How many domestic doubles has the club secured as of 2020?

    a. 10
    b. 7
    c. 4
    d. 2

15. Which campaign year did Madrid win its first domestic double?

    a. 1982-83
    b. 1973-74
    c. 1965-66
    d. 1961-62

16. Real Madrid won the now-defunct Copa Eva Duarte four times.

    a. True
    b. False

17. How many times has Madrid won the Copa del Rey as of 2020?

    a. 19
    b. 17

c. 13

d. 11

18. Which side did the club humble to win its first-ever Supercopa de España?

    a. Getafe CF

    b. Cádiz CF

    c. CA Osasuna

    d. FC Barcelona

19. Which campaign year did Los Blancos win their first La Liga title?

    a. 1960-61

    b. 1954-55

    c. 1942-43

    d. 1931-32

20. Real Madrid holds the record for winning the most Copa del Rey titles.

    a. True

    b. False

QUIZ ANSWERS

1. C – 1905

2. A – True

3. D – Atlético Madrid

4. B – 11

5. B – Valencia CF

6. D – Athletic Bilbao

7. A – True

8. C – 34

9. A – RCD Mallorca

10. A – Real Madrid Castilla

11. D – 23

12. B – False

13. C – Real Zaragoza

14. C – 4

15. D – 1961-62

16. B – False

17. A – 19

18. D – FC Barcelona

19. D – 1931-32

20. B – False

DID YOU KNOW?

1. As of January 2021, Real Madrid has won 66 major domestic trophies, including a record 34 La Liga titles, 19 Copa del Rey, 11 Supercopa de España, one Copa Eva Duarte, and one Copa de La Liga title. The side played its first competitive game on May 13, 1902, when it entered the semi-final of the Campeonato de Copa de S.M. Alfonso XIII and was beaten 3-1 by Barcelona.

2. Real Madrid's record 34 La Liga titles were won in the following seasons: 1931-32, 1932-33, 1953-54, 1954-55, 1956-57, 1957-58, 1960-61, 1961-62, 1962-63, 1963-64, 1964-65, 1966-67, 1967-68, 1968-69, 1971-72, 1974-75, 1975-76, 1977-78, 1978-79, 1979-80, 1985-86, 1986-87, 1987-88, 1988-89, 1989-90, 1994-95, 1996-97, 2000-01, 2002-03, 2006-07, 2007-08, 2011-12, 2016-17, and 2019-20.

3. The Copa del Rey was hoisted by the club 19 times, in 1905, 1906, 1907, 1908, 1917, 1934, 1936, 1946, 1947, 1961-62, 1969-70, 1973-74, 1974-75, 1979-80, 1981-82, 1988-89, 1992-93, 2010-11, and 2013-14.

4. Real Madrid won the Supercopa de España 11 times, in 1988, 1989, 1990, 1993, 1997, 2001, 2003, 2008, 2012, 2017, and 2019-20. The team captured the Copa Eva Duarte, which was the predecessor to the Supercopa de España, in 1947. In addition, the side won one of just four Copa de La

Liga (League Cup) competitions, which were held between 1982 and 1986, by capturing the 1984-85 tournament.

5. The club record for most points in a La Liga season in which two points were awarded for a win was 66 in 44 games in 1986-87. The current high mark for points in a season with three points awarded for a victory is 100 in 38 contests in 2011-12. The club record for fewest points in a season with two points awarded for a win was 17 in 18 outings in 1929-30, while the fewest points in a campaign with three points awarded for a win currently stands at 70 in 42 games in 1995-96.

6. The current Real Madrid record for most goals scored in a La Liga season is 121 in 2011-12; the most goals tallied in all competitions was also in 2011-12, when the side scored 174 times. The highest goal difference for the club in a league season is +89, also in 2011-12. The fewest goals notched in a league campaign was 24 in 1930-31, and the most goals conceded was 71 in the 1950-51 season. The fewest goals conceded in a league campaign was 15 in 1931-32.

7. The most wins in a La Liga season for the club was 32 in 38 games in 2011-12 with the most home victories being 18 in 19 matches in the 1987-88 and 2009-10 seasons. The club record for most away wins in a campaign was 16 in 19 games, also in 2011-12. The most games drawn in a campaign was 15 in 34 outings in 1978-79 with the fewest draws being one in 18 games in the 1929 season and one in

22 games in 1934-35 and 1939-40. The most losses in a season was 13 in 34 outings in 1973-74. The team's fewest league wins in a season was seven in 18 matches in 1929-30. And the fewest defeats in a season was none when the team went unbeaten in 18 outings in 1931-32.

8. When it comes to current record domestic wins for the side, Real Madrid's biggest league and home triumph was 11-2 against Elche in 1959-60. The biggest cup victory was an 11-1 demolition job of Barcelona in the 1943 Copa del Generalísimo event. Real's biggest away La Liga victories were 7-1 against Real Zaragoza in 1987-88 and 8-2 over Deportivo La Coruña in 2014-15.

9. Real Madrid has also been on the receiving end of some lopsided beatings, with their record La Liga and away league loss being 8-1 against Español in 1929-30. The worst domestic cup humiliation was at home in the form of a 6-0 hammering by Valencia in the 1998-99 Copa del Rey competition. The side's record home La Liga defeat was 7-0 by Athletic Bilbao in 1930-31.

10. One of Real Madrid's most embarrassing losses came at the feet of third-tier club Alcoyano, when they were humbled 2-1 away in the round of 32 in the Copa del Rey. The upset took place on January 20, 2021, after Real led 1-0 until the 80th minute. Alcoyano leveled the match and then won it in the 115th minute as the contest went into extra time. The winning goal came with Alcoyano down to 10 men as Ramón López was ejected in the 109th minute after

receiving a second yellow card. It was the fourth time in history that Real was knocked out of the Copa del Rey by a Segunda División B team.

CHAPTER 11:

EUROPE & BEYOND

QUIZ TIME!

1. Which club did Madrid defeat in its first European Cup final in 1955-56?

    a. Hibernian FC
    b. AC Milan
    c. Stade de Reims
    d. Paris Saint-Germain

2. Real Madrid participated in the 2017 MLS All-Star Game and won 4-2 on penalties.

    a. True
    b. False

3. What year did the club win its first Intercontinental Cup?

    a. 1960
    b. 1972
    c. 1998
    d. 2002

4. Which club did Real defeat to win the 2014 FIFA Club World Cup final?

   a. Cruz Azul
   b. San Lorenzo
   c. Entente Sportive Sétifienne
   d. Auckland City FC

5. How many times have Los Blancos won the UEFA Super Cup, as of 2020?

   a. 7
   b. 6
   c. 4
   d. 2

6. Which club did Real Madrid face in the 2002 UEFA Super Cup?

   a. Liverpool FC
   b. FC Porto
   c. Bayern Munich
   d. Feyenoord

7. Real Madrid won the inaugural European Cup competition.

   a. True
   b. False

8. Which Argentine team did Madrid face in the only Copa Iberoamericana competition held in 1994?

   a. Huracán
   b. Newell's Old Boys

c. Boca Juniors

d. San Lorenzo

9. Real downed which side to win their first Intercontinental Cup?

    a. S.L. Benfica

    b. CA Peñarol

    c. Celtic FC

    d. Ajax

10. How many doubles involving an international trophy has Real Madrid won as of 2020?

    a. 3

    b. 4

    c. 6

    d. 9

11. Which club did Madrid beat in the 2016 FIFA Club World Cup final?

    a. Kashima Antlers

    b. Atlético Nacional

    c. Inter Milan

    d. Manchester City

12. Real Madrid secured its first treble in 1957-58.

    a. True

    b. False

13. Which club did the side face in the 2002 Intercontinental Cup final?

a. São Paulo FC

b. Bayern Munich

c. Boca Juniors

d. Club Olimpia

14. How many times has Real Madrid won the UEFA Europa League, as of 2020?

   a. 6

   b. 0

   c. 4

   d. 2

15. How many times has the club hoisted the European Cup/UEFA Champions League, as of 2020?

   a. 6

   b. 10

   c. 13

   d. 16

16. Real Madrid shares the record for most Intercontinental Cups won with three titles.

   a. True

   b. False

17. Which club did Madrid humble in the 2014-15 UEFA Champions League final?

   a. Juventus

   b. Atlético Madrid

   c. Borussia Dortmund

   d. Olympique Marseille

18. How many consecutive seasons did the club successfully defend its European Cup title beginning in 1957?

    a. 2
    b. 4
    c. 5
    d. 6

19. Which club did Los Blancos meet in the 2017 UEFA Super Cup?

    a. Juventus
    b. Sevilla FC
    c. Dynamo Kyiv
    d. Manchester United

20. Real Madrid has won the Latin Cup twice.

    a. True
    b. False

QUIZ ANSWERS

1. C – Stade de Reims

2. A – True

3. A – 1960

4. B – San Lorenzo

5. C – 4

6. D – Feyenoord

7. A – True

8. C – Boca Juniors

9. B – CA Peñarol

10. C – 6

11. A – Kashima Antlers

12. B – False

13. D – Club Olimpia

14. D – 2

15. C – 13

16. A – True

17. A – Juventus

18. B – 4

19. D – Manchester United

20. A – True

DID YOU KNOW?

1. Real Madrid currently holds the record for the most European Cup/UEFA Champions League triumphs at 13 and has won a total of 26 major European/international trophies, making it the most successful club in the world in this category. This total also includes a record four FIFA Club World championships, four UEFA Super Cups, three Intercontinental Cups, and two UEFA Cups/Europa Leagues.

2. The club first participated in a European competition in 1955, when it competed in the Latin Cup as champions of Spain. The Latin Cup ran from 1949 to 1957 as a tournament designed for club teams from the Latin European nations, Spain, Portugal, Italy, and France. It was also known as Coupe Latine, Coppa Latina, Taça Latina, and Copa Latina. Real Madrid participated in the event in 1955 and 1957 and hoisted the trophy both times.

3. Real Madrid also entered the European Cup/Champions League tournament in 1955 and since then has competed in every UEFA-organized competition other than the Intertoto Cup. The team won the inaugural European Cup tournament and is currently the only club to win the title five consecutive times, as it captured the trophy the first five seasons the competition ran.

4. The European Cup/Champions League triumphs for Real Madrid came in 1955-56, 1956-57, 1957-58, 1958-59, 1959-60, 1965-66, 1997-98, 1999-2000, 2001-02, 2013-14, 2015-16, 2016-17, and 2017-18. The UEFA Cup/Europa League was won in 1984-85 and 1985-86, while the European/UEFA Super Cup was hoisted in 2002, 2014, 2016, and 2017. The team captured the Intercontinental Cup in 1960, 1998, and 2002, and its FIFA Club World Cup victories were in 2014, 2016, 2017, and 2018.

5. Midfield legend Zinedine Zidane scored one of the greatest goals in a European Cup/Champions League final at Hampden Park in Glasgow, Scotland, in 2002 against Bayer Leverkusen of Germany. The French international star was in his prime at this time. In the 45th minute of a 1-1 game, Zidane was loitering around the opponent's 18-yard box when teammate Roberto Carlos delivered a hanging cross. Zidane swiveled his hips and met the ball with a thunderous left-footed volley that sent it flying past goalkeeper Hans-Jorg Butt and into the back of the net. It's arguably the best Champions League goal ever, and it gave Real Madrid its ninth European crown.

6. The only European competition Real Madrid participated in and didn't win was the European Cup Winners' Cup, which was renamed the UEFA Cup Winners' Cup in 1994-95. This tournament was played annually from 1960 to 1999 by the winners of all European domestic cup competitions. Starting in 1972, the winner of the Cup

Winners' Cup played the winner of the European Cup/Champions League for the UEFA Super Cup. Real Madrid was beaten 2-1 by Chelsea of England in the 1971 final and 2-1 in extra time by Aberdeen of Scotland in the 1983 final.

7. As of December 9, 2020, Real Madrid had played 566 combined games in the European Cup/Champions League, UEFA Cup Winners' Cup, UEFA Cup/Europa League, UEFA Super Cup, Intercontinental Cup, and the FIFA Club World Cup. Their overall record stood at 331 wins, 99 draws, and 136 losses with 1,206 goals for and 616 allowed. This gave the club a goal difference of 588 and a winning percentage of 58.48.

8. Real Madrid's record European tournament win was a 9-0 whitewash against Boldklubben 1913 of Denmark in the 1961-62 European Cup. The club's biggest defeat in a European competition was a 5-0 drubbing at the feet of FC Kaiserslautern of Germany in the 1981-82 UEFA Cup and 5-0 to AC Milan of Italy in the 1988-89 European Cup.

9. The following players won the Ballon d'Or while playing for Real Madrid: Alfredo Di Stéfano, 1957, 1959; Raymond Kopa, 1958; Luís Figo, 2000; Ronaldo, 2002; Fábio Cannavaro, 2006; Cristiano Ronaldo, 2016, 2017; Luka Modrić, 2018. Those who were named FIFA World Player of the Year have been: Luís Figo, 2001; Ronaldo, 2002; Zinedine Zidane, 2003; and Fábio Cannavaro, 2006. Those who won the FIFA Ballon d'Or were Cristiano Ronaldo in

2013 and 2014 and the Best FIFA Men's Player was also won by Cristiano Ronaldo in 2016 and 2017 and by Luka Modrić in 2018.

10. Just two Real Madrid players have won the European Golden Boot award as of 2020. Hugo Sánchez took it home in 1989-90 with 38 goals, while Cristiano Ronaldo won it in 2010-11 with 40 goals, in 2013-14 with 31, and in 2014-15 with 48. The UEFA Club Footballer of the Year was won by Fernando Redondo in 2000 and Zinedine Zidane in 2002. The UEFA Best Player in Europe Award was captured by Cristiano Ronaldo in 2014, 2016, and 2017, and by Luka Modrić in 2018.

CHAPTER 12:

TOP SCORERS

QUIZ TIME!

1. Who was the first player to lead La Liga in scoring as a member of Real Madrid?

   a. Gaspar Rubio

   b. Manuel Olivares

   c. Jaime Lazcano

   d. Luis Regueiro

2. Alfredo Di Stéfano once led La Liga in scoring in six consecutive seasons.

   a. True

   b. False

3. Who is the club's all-time leader in goal scoring in all competitions as of 2020?

   a. Cristiano Ronaldo

   b. Alfredo Di Stéfano

   c. Raúl

   d. Santillana

4. Who was the first Real Madrid player to win the European Golden Boot award?

   a. Ronaldo Luís Nazário
   b. Karim Benzema
   c. Hugo Sánchez
   d. Ferenc Puskás

5. Which player led La Liga in scoring with 25 goals in 2006-07?

   a. Gonzalo Higuaín
   b. Ruud van Nistelrooy
   c. Robinho
   d. Raúl

6. How many goals did Cristiano Ronaldo score for Real Madrid?

   a. 385
   b. 427
   c. 451
   d. 463

7. Ronaldo Luís Nazário once led the squad in scoring in four consecutive La Liga seasons.

   a. True
   b. False

8. How many goals did Emilio Butragueño tally to lead the club and La Liga in 1990-91?

   a. 19
   b. 23

c. 26

d. 28

9. Which player scored 125 goals in all competitions in only 143 matches?

    a. Ruud van Nistelrooy

    b. Joseíto

    c. Gareth Bale

    d. Pahiño

10. Which player never led La Liga in scoring while playing for Real Madrid?

    a. Pahiño

    b. Juanito

    c. Gonzalo Higuaín

    d. Iván Zamorano

11. How many seasons did Ferenc Puskás lead La Liga in scoring while playing for Madrid?

    a. 2

    b. 4

    c. 5

    d. 7

12. Gaspar Rubio led the club in its debut La Liga campaign, with 12 goals.

    a. True

    b. False

13. Which player scored 290 goals in all competitions with the squad?

    a. Santillana

    b. Francisco Gento

    c. Emilio Butragueño

    d. Hugo Sánchez

14. How many goals did Alfredo Di Stéfano net to lead La Liga in 1956-57?

    a. 20

    b. 25

    c. 28

    d. 31

15. Which player led La Liga in scoring in back-to-back seasons, 1968 to 1970?

    a. Manuel Velázquez

    b. Ramón Grosso

    c. Amancio Amaro

    d. Pirri

16. As of 2020, Madrid has had 17 different players lead La Liga in scoring.

    a. True

    b. False

17. How many goals did Cristiano Ronaldo tally in the 2014-15 La Liga season?

    a. 27

    b. 32

c. 41

d. 48

18. Who scored 26 La Liga goals to lead the side in 1996-97?

    a. Predrag Mijatović

    b. Fernando Morientes

    c. Davor Šuker

    d. Fernando Hierro

19. How many goals did Gaspar Rubio rack up to lead La Liga in 1932-33?

    a. 15

    b. 11

    c. 23

    d. 9

20. In the 1981-82 La Liga season, three players tied for the team lead with nine goals each.

    a. True

    b. False

QUIZ ANSWERS

1. B – Manuel Olivares

2. B – False

3. A – Cristiano Ronaldo

4. C – Hugo Sánchez

5. B – Ruud van Nistelrooy

6. C – 451

7. A – True

8. A – 19

9. D – Pahiño

10. C – Gonzalo Higuaín

11. B – 4

12. A – True

13. A – Santillana

14. D – 31

15. C – Amancio Amaro

16. B – False

17. D – 48

18. C – Davor Šuker

19. A – 15

20. A – True

DID YOU KNOW?

1. Portuguese international forward Cristiano Ronaldo holds the record for most goals scored for the club with 451 in 438 competitive appearances, according to the club's official website. Ronaldo played with the squad from 2009 to 2018 and tallied 312 times in La Liga, 105 times in the European Champions League, 22 in the Copa del Rey, six in the Club World Cup, four in the Spanish Super Cup, and two in the UEFA Super Cup. Ronaldo also helped the side capture 16 major trophies and won numerous individual awards with the side, including four Ballons d'Or and three La Liga titles and European Golden Boots. He was named UEFA's Best Player in Europe three times. He holds most of the club's scoring records, including most goals in all competitions in a season with 61, and he will go down in history as one of the greatest players ever.

2. Raúl González was a Spanish international striker known simply as "Raúl" and was one of the greatest finishers in Real Madrid and La Liga history. He was quite creative on the pitch for the club between 1994 and 2010 and, when he left, he was the second-highest scorer in team history with 323 goals under his belt in a club-record 741 contests. The former skipper helped the squad win the Champions League three times and the La Liga on six occasions. In addition, he won two Intercontinental Cups, a UEFA Super Cup, and four Supercopa de España championships.

3. Alfredo Di Stéfano was born in Argentina to Italian parents and moved to Europe as a youngster. Due to his heritage, he played internationally for Argentina, Colombia, and Spain. He played between 1943 and 1966 with his best years coming at Real Madrid between 1953 and 1964 when he notched 308 goals in 396 contests. The striker helped the team win five consecutive European Cups and scored in each of the five finals. Di Stéfano was one of the world's most complete players. He helped Real win 17 trophies as a player, and he later managed the squad and was named its honorary president. He also captured the Ballon d'Or in 1957 and 1959.

4. With 290 goals in 645 games with Real Madrid, Spanish international forward Carlos Alonso González or "Santillana," as he was known, will forever be remembered as one of the club's top scorers and for his partnership with Juanito. He helped the side win nine La Liga titles and 16 trophies overall after arriving in 1971 at the age of 19. He had previously won the Golden Boot in the Spanish Segunda División with Racing Santander and scored 186 times with Real in the league through 1988. When he retired, only Alfredo Di Stéfano had scored more goals for the club.

5. French international striker Karim Benzema kicked off his pro career with Olympique Lyonnais and joined Real Madrid in 2009 to play alongside fellow newcomers Kaká and Cristiano Ronaldo. In 2011, Benzema entered the

record book for notching the fastest El Clásico goal ever when he struck after just 21 seconds against Barcelona. As of February 2021, he was still with Los Blancos and had netted over 260 goals in more than 500 matches. He has helped the squad hoist 18 trophies, including the European Champions League and FIFA Club World Cup four times and three La Liga titles.

6. Ferenc Puskás of Hungary was once the top national scorer on the globe and finished his career with 84 goals in 85 games for his homeland. While Juventus was eager to sign him, Real Madrid beat them to the punch when he joined in 1958 as a 31-year-old. Some fans were unhappy with the signing because they believed Puskás was overweight and too old. He proved them wrong by posting 242 goals in 262 outings, including four hat-tricks in his first campaign with the team. Puskás helped the side win five La Liga and three European Cup titles, as well as an Intercontinental Cup and Copa del Rey by 1967. He led La Liga in scoring on four occasions. The FIFA named its best goal of the year award after Puskás.

7. Hugo Sánchez was one of Real Madrid's greatest finishers, with 208 goals in 282 outings between 1985 and 1992. The Mexican international forward was well-known for his acrobatic shots and somersaults after netting a goal. He joined the team from Atlético Madrid and won the UEFA Cup and the La Liga Golden Boot with 22 goals in his first year with Real. With Sánchez in the lineup, the side won

five straight La Liga crowns and four other trophies. He also ended up with a European and four La Liga Golden Boots and was named the best footballer of the 20th century in Central and North Central America by the IFFHS.

8. Speedy outside-left Francisco "Paco" Gento was another all-time Real Madrid great who starred for both club and country. His La Liga career kicked off with Racing Santander in 1952 before he signed with Los Blancos the next year. He stayed with the side until 1971. He was an excellent technical player who took great pleasure in setting up his teammates as well as scoring goals. Gento notched 182 of them in 600 games with the club, and the former captain helped Real reach the European Cup final eight times, winning six of them, a playing record. He also won the La Liga 12 times with the team, along with another six major trophies.

9. José Martínez Sánchez, known simply as "Pirri," spent 1964 to 1980 with Real Madrid while chipping in with 172 goals in 561 contests. He was known for his versatility because he could play any outfield position on the pitch and played the 1971 European Cup Winners' Cup final with his arm in a sling and the 1975 Copa del Rey final with a broken jaw. The Spanish international won the La Liga title in his first season in Madrid and went on to win nine more, as well as a European Cup and four Copa del Rey championships. After hanging up his boots, Pirri joined the club's medical and coaching staff.

10. Emilio Butragueño tallied 171 goals in 463 official matches with Real Madrid between 1982 and 1995 and helped the side haul in 15 pieces of silverware, including six La Liga titles. The Spanish international striker was known for his tremendous dribbling skills, intelligence, and creativity. Nicknamed "The Vulture," he signed with Real after playing in the club's youth system. He made his senior debut in February 1984 under manager Alfredo Di Stéfano and scored twice while setting up another goal. Butragueño won the Bravo Trophy for Europe's best under-24 player two straight years and captured the La Liga Golden Boot in 1990-91 with 19 goals. He later served as the club's director of football, vice president, and head of public relations.

CONCLUSION

It's far from over, but what you have in front of you is the updated history of Real Madrid from the club's beginning in 1902 right up to February 2021.

Being one of the oldest and most successful soccer clubs in the world, with hundreds of players having worn the team's kit, it's impossible to include everybody. Therefore, we apologize if your favorite player, event, or manager has been left out. Most of the big stars and important figures are included, though, from Arthur Johnson in the early days to current team captain Sergio Ramos and manager Zinedine Zidane.

We hope you've enjoyed looking back through the club's mesmerizing history, records, transfers, and achievements, and perhaps you learned something you may not have been aware of. We've presented the information in a lighthearted manner as a way to entertain you along the way.

Equipped with 12 different chapters featuring dozens of challenging quiz questions and educational "Did You Know" facts, you should now be ready, willing, and able to challenge fellow Los Blancos fans and other soccer supporters to the ultimate Real Madrid trivia showdown.